University Colloquium: A Sustainable Future

Florida Gulf Coast University

Copley Custom Textbooks
An imprint of XanEdu Publishing, Inc.

ISBN 13: 978-1-58152-761-2
ISBN 10: 1-58152-761-6

Cover Design by Bob Klein, Florida Gulf Coast University. Photos by Annette Snapp, Ph.D.

Acknowledgments:

pp. 1–14: From *Last Child in the Woods* by Richard Louv. Copyright © 2005 by Richard Louv. Reprinted by permission of Algonquin Books of Chapel Hill. All rights reserved.

pp 15–37: From *Collapse: How Societies Choose to Fail or Succeed* by Jared Diamond. Copyright © 2005 by Jared Diamond. Used by permission of Viking Penguin, a division of Penguin Group (USA) Inc.

pp. 38–57: From *Tomorrow's Biodiversity* by Vandana Shiva. Copyright © 2000. Published by Thames and Hudson, Inc.

pp. 58–77: From *A Sand County Almanac: With Essays on Conservation from Round River* by Aldo Leopold. Copyright © 1949 by Oxford University Press. Reprinted by permission of the publisher via the Copyright Clearance Center.

pp. 78–103: From *The Swamp: The Everglades, Florida, and the Politics of Paradise* by Michael Grunwald. Copyright © 2006 by Michael Grunwald. All rights reserved. Reprinted by permission of Simon & Schuster, Inc.

pp. 104–149: From *The Everglades: River of Grass* by Marjory Stoneman Douglas. Copyright © 1988 by Pineapple Press. Reprinted by permission.

Copley Custom Textbooks
An imprint of XanEdu Publishing, Inc.
138 Great Road
Acton, MA 01720
800-562-2147

Contents

Excerpt from *Last Child in the Woods*

Nature-Deficit Disorder and the Restorative Environment

Richard Louv

With idealism and trepidation, a graduating college student anticipates becoming a teacher; but she is puzzled and upset by the school environment she experienced during her training. "With all of the testing in schools there is no time for physical education, let alone exploring the outdoors," she says. "In one of my kindergarten classes, the kids get to run to a fence and then run back. That's their P.E. They have to stay on the blacktop, or they can use one of the two swings available." She doesn't understand why P.E. is so limited, or why the playground can't be more conducive to natural play. Many educators share her sentiment.

At least her school has recess. In the United States, as the federal and state governments and local school boards have pushed for higher test scores in the first decade of the twenty-first century, nearly 40 percent of American elementary schools either eliminated or were considering eliminating recess. In the era of test-centric education reform and growing fear of liability, many districts considered recess a waste of potential academic time or too risky. "Lifers at Leavenworth get more time in the exercise yard," commented *Sports Illustrated* columnist Steve Rushin. School-based physical education was already on the wane.

Between 1991 and 2003, the percentage of students who attended physical education class dropped from 42 percent to only 28 percent. Some states now allow students to earn P.E. credits *online*. Field trips were also cut. Even as school districts decreased students' experiences beyond the classroom walls, they increased the number of school hours. Ironically, the detachment of education from the physical world not only coincided with the dramatic rise in life-threatening childhood obesity but also with a growing body of evidence that links physical exercise and experience in nature to mental acuity and concentration.

Now, for some good news. Studies suggest that nature may be useful as a therapy for Attention Deficit Hyperactivity Disorder (ADHD), used with or, when appropriate, even replacing medications or behavioral therapies. Some researchers now recommend that parents and educators make available more nature experiences—especially green places—to children with ADHD, and thereby support their attentional functioning and minimize their symptoms. Indeed, this research inspires use of the broader term "nature-deficit disorder" as away to help us better understand what many children experience, whether or not they have been diagnosed with ADHD. Again, I am not using the term nature-deficit disorder in a scientific or clinical sense. Certainly no academic researchers use the term, yet; nor do they attribute ADHD entirely to a nature deficit. But based on accumulating scientific evidence, I believe the concept—or hypothesis—of nature-deficit disorder is appropriate and useful as a layperson's description of one factor that may aggravate attentional difficulties for many children.

First, consider the diagnosis and current treatments of choice.

Nearly 8 million children in the U.S. suffer from mental disorders, and ADHD is one of the more prevalent ones. The disorder often develops before age seven, and is usually diagnosed between the ages of eight and ten. (Some people use the acronym ADD, for attention deficit disorder, to mean ADHD without the hyperactive component. But ADHD is the more accepted medical diagnosis.) Children with the syndrome are restless and have trouble paying attention, listening, following directions, and focusing on tasks. They may also be aggressive, even antisocial, and may suffer from academic failure. Or, in the language of the American Psychiatric Association: "The essential feature of ADHD is a persistent pattern of inattention and/ or hyperactivity, impulsivity . . . more frequently displayed and more severe than is typically observed in individuals at a comparable level of development." Some of the uninformed public tends to believe that poor parenting and other social factors produce the immature behavior associated with ADHD, but ADHD is now considered by many researchers to be an organic disorder associated with differences in the brain morphology of children.

Critics charge that often-prescribed stimulant medications such as methylphenidate (Ritalin) and amphetamines (Dexedrine), though necessary in many cases, are overprescribed, perhaps as much as 10 to 40 percent of the time. Methylphenidate is a central nervous system stimulant and shares many of the pharmacological effects of amphetamine, methamphetamine, and cocaine. Contrasting sharply with medical practices elsewhere in the world, use of such stimulants in the United States increased 600 percent between 1990 and 1995, and continues to rise in numbers, especially for younger children. Between 2000 and 2003, spending on ADHD for preschoolers increased 369 percent. Both boys and girls are diagnosed with ADHD, but approximately 90 percent of the young people placed on medication—often at the suggestion of school officials—are boys.

One child psychiatrist explains: "My prejudice is that girls with ADHD whose symptoms are similar to boys with typical symptoms of ADHD are not common." Notice that he said "prejudice." Much about ADHD remains a medical and political mystery.

The massive increase in ADHD diagnoses and treatment may, in fact, be a matter of recognition: ADHD has been there all the time, called by other names or missed entirely, causing suffering for children and their families. Another explanation boils down to availability:

three decades ago, the currently used medications were not widely known or as intensely marketed by pharmaceutical companies, and not yet fully trusted by physicians—and we're lucky to have them now. Nonetheless, the use of such medications and the causes of ADHD are still in dispute. As of this writing, the latest culprit is television. The first study to link television-watching to this disorder was published in April 2004. Children's Hospital and Regional Medical Center in Seattle maintains that each hour of TV watched per day by preschoolers increases by 10 percent the likelihood that they will develop concentration problems and other symptoms of attention-deficit disorders by age seven.

This information is disturbing. But television is only part of the larger environmental/cultural change in our lifetime: namely, that rapid move from a rural to a highly urbanized culture. In an agricultural society, or during a time of exploration and settlement, or hunting and gathering—which is to say, most of mankind's history—energetic boys were particularly prized for their strength, speed, and agility. As mentioned earlier, as recently as the 1950s, most families still had some kind of agricultural connection. Many of these children, girls as well as boys, would have been directing their energy and physicality in constructive ways: doing farm chores, baling hay, splashing in the swimming hole, climbing trees, racing to the sandlot for a game of baseball. Their unregimented play would have been steeped in nature.

The "Restorative Environment"

Even without corroborating evidence or institutional help, many parents notice significant changes in their children's stress levels and hyperactivity when they spend time outside. "My son is still on Ritalin, but he's so much calmer in the outdoors that we're seriously considering moving to the mountains," one mother tells me. Could it simply be that he needs more physical activity? "No, he gets that, in sports," she says. Similarly, the back page of an October issue of *San Francisco* magazine displays a vivid photograph of a small boy, eyes wide with excitement and joy, leaping and running on a great expanse of California beach, storm clouds and towering waves behind him. A short article explains that the boy was hyperactive, he had been kicked out of his school, and his parents had not known what to do with him—but they had observed how nature engaged and soothed him. So for years they took their son to beaches, forests, dunes, and rivers to let nature do its work.

The photograph was taken in 1907. The boy was Ansel Adams. "Our brains are set up for an agrarian, nature-oriented existence that came into focus five thousand years ago," says Michael Gurian, a family therapist and best-selling author of *The Good Son* and *The Wonder of Boys*. "Neurologically, human beings haven't caught up with today's over-stimulating environment. The brain is strong and flexible, so 70 to 80 percent of kids adapt fairly well. But the rest don't. Getting kids out in nature can make a difference. We know this anecdotally, though we can't prove it yet."

New studies may offer that proof.

This research builds on the well-established attention-restoration theory, developed by a husband-and-wife research team, Stephen and Rachel Kaplan. Environmental psychologists at the University of Michigan, the Kaplans were inspired by philosopher and psychologist William James. In 1890, James described two kinds of attention: directed attention and fascination (i.e., involuntary attention). In the early 1970s, the Kaplans began a nine-year study for the U.S. Forest Service. They followed participants in an Outward Bound–like wilderness program, which took people into the wilds for up to two weeks. During these treks or afterward, subjects reported experiencing a sense of peace and an ability to think more clearly; they also reported that just being in nature was more restorative than the physically challenging activities, such as rock climbing, for which such programs are mainly known.

The positive effect of what the Kaplans came to call "the restorative environment" was vastly greater than the Kaplans expected it to be. According to the Kaplans' research, too much directed attention leads to what they call "directed-attention fatigue," marked by impulsive behavior, agitation, irritation, and inability to concentrate. Directed-attention fatigue occurs because neural inhibitory mechanisms become fatigued by blocking competing stimuli. As Stephen Kaplan explained in the journal *Monitor on Psychology*, "If you can find an environment where the attention is automatic, you allow directed attention to rest. And that means an environment that's strong on fascination." The fascination factor associated with nature is restorative, and it helps relieve people from directed-attention fatigue. Indeed, according to the Kaplans, nature can be the most effective source of such restorative relief.

In a paper presented to the American Psychological Society in 1993, the Kaplans surveyed more than twelve hundred corporate and state office workers. Those with a window view of trees, bushes, or large lawns experienced significantly less frustration and more work enthusiasm than those employees without such views. Like similar studies on stress reduction, this study demonstrated that a person does not have to live in the wilderness to reap nature's psychological benefits—including the ability to work better and think more clearly.

Subsequent research has supported the Kaplans' attention-restoration theory. For example, Terry A. Hartig, an associate professor of applied psychology at the Institute for Housing and Urban Research at Uppsala University in Gävle, Sweden, along with other researchers, compared three groups of backpacking enthusiasts; a group who went on a wilderness backpacking trip showed improved proofreading performance, while those who went on an urban vacation or took no vacation showed no improvement. In 2001, Hartig demonstrated that nature can help people recover from "normal psychological wear and tear"—but nature also improves the capacity to pay attention. Hartig emphasizes that he does not test the extremes—say, the Sierras versus East Los Angeles. Rather, his studies have focused on what he describes as "typical local conditions." As described in *Monitor on Psychology*, Hartig asked participants to complete a forty-minute sequence of tasks designed to exhaust their directed-attention capacity. After the attention-fatiguing tasks, Hartig then randomly assigned participants to spend forty minutes "walking in a local nature preserve, walking in an urban area, or sitting quietly while reading magazines and listening to music," the journal reported. "After this period, those who had walked in the nature preserve performed better than the other participants on a standard proofreading task. They also reported more positive emotions and less anger."

Nature's Ritalin

Attention-restoration theory applies to everyone, regardless of age. But what about children, especially those with ADHD?

"By bolstering children's attention resources, green spaces may enable children to think more clearly and cope more effectively with life stress," writes Nancy Wells, assistant professor at the New York State College of Human Ecology. In 2000, Wells conducted a study that found that being close to nature, in general, helps boost a child's attention span. When children's cognitive functioning was compared before and after they moved from poor- to better-quality housing adjacent to natural, green spaces, "profound differences emerged in their attention capacities even when the effects of the improved housing were taken into account," according to Wells.

Swedish researchers compared children within two day-care settings: at one, the quiet play area was surrounded by tall buildings, with low plants and a brick path; at the other, the play area, based on an "outdoors in all weather" theme, was set in an orchard surrounded by pasture and woods and was adjacent to an overgrown garden with tall trees and rocks. The study revealed that children in the "green" day care, who played outside every day, regardless of weather, had better motor coordination and more ability to concentrate.

Some of the most important work in this area has been done at the Human-Environment Research Laboratory at the University of Illinois. Andrea Faber Taylor, Frances Kuo, and William C. Sullivan have found that green outdoor spaces foster creative play, improve children's access to positive adult interaction—and relieve the symptoms of attention-deficit disorders. The greener the setting, the more the relief. By comparison, activities indoors, such as watching TV or outdoors in paved, non-green areas, increase these children's symptoms.

In a survey of the families of ADHD children ages seven to twelve, parents or guardians were asked to identify after-school or weekend activities that left their child functioning especially well or particularly poorly. Activities were coded as "green" or "not green." Green activities, for example, included camping and fishing. Not-green activities included watching television, playing video games, doing homework. Some activities, such as rollerblading, were labeled ambiguous. The controls in this study were more complex than space allows me to describe, but suffice it to say, the research team was careful to account for variables. They found that greenery in a child's everyday environment, even views of green through a window, specifically reduces attention-deficit symptoms. While outdoor activities in general help, settings with trees and grass are the most beneficial. As they reported in the journal *Environment and Behavior*, "compared to the aftereffects of play in paved outdoor or indoor areas, activities in natural, green settings were far more likely to leave ADD children better able to focus, concentrate. Activities that left ADD children in worse shape were far more likely to occur indoors or outdoors in spaces devoid of greenery."

They also found, that the positive influence of near-home nature on concentration may be more pronounced for girls (ages six to nine) than for boys. On average, the greener a girl's view from home, the better she concentrates, the less she acts impulsively, and the longer she can delay gratification. This helps her do better in school, handle peer pressure, and avoid dangerous, unhealthy, or problem behaviors. She is more likely to behave in ways that foster success in life, according to the researchers. Perhaps, if girls are less biologically prone to ADHD, as some mental health professionals believe, they may exhibit milder symptoms and may also have a more robust, healthy response to the treatment—whether pharmaceutical or green.

Based on the study, the University of Illinois issued this informal advice regarding girls to parents, caregivers, and others. The information also applies to boys:

- Encourage girls to study or play in rooms with a view of nature.
- Encourage children to play outdoors in green spaces, and advocate recess in green schoolyards. This may be especially helpful for renewing children's concentration.
- Plant and care for trees and vegetation at your residence, or encourage the owner to do so.
- Value and care for the trees in your community. Caring for trees means caring for people.

In addition to its work in the housing projects of inner-city Chicago, the Human-Environment Research Laboratory has also examined nature's impact on children with ADHD in middle-class settings. There, as in the public housing development, parents reported that their children exhibited fewer symptoms of ADHD after spending time in green surroundings. "You could say that the kids who had greener settings were just richer," says Kuo. "But that doesn't explain the fact that even rich kids do better after being in green settings. . . ." In the report:

> Participants were asked if they had had any experiences, either positive or negative, related to any aftereffects of green settings on their child's attention. One parent said she had recently begun taking her son to the local park for 30 minutes each morning before school because the weather was nice, and they "had some time to kill." She then said, "Come to think of it, I have noticed his attitude toward going to school has been better, and his schoolwork has been better this past week. I think it's because spending time at the park is pleasurable, peaceful, quiet, calming."

Another parent reported that his son could hit golf balls or fish for hours, and that during these times the boy was "very relaxed" and his attention-deficit symptoms minimal. "When I read the results of your study, they hit me in the face," he told the researchers. "I thought, yes, I've seen this!"

So had some of the parents I interviewed. Noticing that their children's ADHD symptoms were calmed by natural settings, they applied common sense; they were already encouraging their kids to spend more time outdoors, and they felt affirmed when I told them about the Illinois studies.

Taylor's and Kuo's more recent research findings are equally provocative. According to an unpublished study (which Taylor emphasizes is "a work in progress"), attention performance for unmedicated children clinically diagnosed with ADHD was better after a simple twenty-minute walk in a park, with a natural setting, than it was after a walk through well-kept downtown and residential areas.

Expanding such knowledge, and applying it in practical ways, will be the next challenge. Although today's common medications for ADHD offer temporary gains, including sustained attention and academic productivity, these medications may do little for a child's long-term success, either socially or academically. The medications can also have unpleasant side effects, among them sleep disruption, depression, and growth suppression of approximately half an inch per year on average, as reported in a large randomized trial funded by the National Institute of Mental Health. A second class of treatment—behavioral therapies—teaches children how to self-monitor attention and impulsive behavior, but the success of these therapies has been mixed.

More time in nature—combined with less television and more stimulating play and educational settings—may go a long way toward reducing attention deficits in children, and, just as important, increasing their joy in life. Researchers at the Human-Environment Research Laboratory believe that their findings point to nature therapy as a potential third course of treatment, applied either in concert with medication and/or behavioral therapy, or on its own. Behavioral therapy and nature therapy, if used collaboratively, might teach the young how to visualize positive experiences in nature when they need a calming tool. One psychiatrist who works with ADHD children relates how he sometimes slides into mild depressions. "I grew up fly-fishing in Michigan, and that was how I found peace as a child," he says. "So, when I begin to feel depressed, I use self-hypnosis to go there again, to call up those memories." He calls them "meadow memories." Though he is a firm believer in the proper use of the currently available medications for ADHD, he is encouraged by the possibility that nature therapy might offer him another professional tool. And, as Kuo points out, prescribing "green time" for the treatment of ADHD has other advantages: it's widely accessible, free of side effects, nonstigmatizing, and inexpensive.

If it's true that nature therapy reduces the symptoms of ADHD, then the converse may also be true: ADHD may be a set of symptoms aggravated by lack of exposure to nature. By this line of thinking, many children may benefit from medications, but the real disorder is less in the child than it is in the imposed, artificial environment. Viewed from this angle, the society that has disengaged the child from nature is most certainly disordered, if well-meaning. To take nature and natural play away from children may be tantamount to withholding oxygen.

An expanded application of attention-restoration theory would be useful in the design of homes, classrooms, and curricula. New York's Central Park, the first professionally designed urban park in America, was originally seen as a necessary aid to both civic consciousness and public health. It was construed as a place where all New Yorkers, regardless of class, age, or health, would benefit from fresh air. If nature-deficit disorder, as a hypothetical condition, affects all children (and adults) whether or not they have some biological propensity for attention deficit, then nature therapy at the societal and individual levels will do the greatest good for the greatest number of people.

Research on the impact of nature experiences on attention disorders and on wider aspects of child health and development is in its infancy, and easily challenged. Scientists doing some of the best of this research are the first to point that out. "For many of us, intuition emphatically asserts that nature is good for children," write Taylor and Kuo, in an overview of the research to date. "Beyond these intuitions, there are also well-reasoned theoretical arguments as to why humans in general—and therefore children—might have an inborn need for contact with nature." Yes, more research is needed, but we do not have to wait for it. As Taylor and Kuo argue, "Given the pattern of statistically reliable findings all pointing the same direction and persisting across different subpopulations of children, different settings, and in spite of design weaknesses, at some point it becomes more parsimonious to accept the fact that nature does promote healthy child development." If, as a growing body of evidence recommends, "contact with nature is as important to children as good nutrition and adequate sleep, then current trends in children's access to nature need to be addressed."

Even the most extensive research is unlikely to capture the full benefits of direct, natural experience. One aspect sure to elude measurement—a phenomenon that will be discussed later in these pages—is the contribution of nature to the spiritual life of the child, and therefore to the adult. This we know: As the sign over Albert Einstein's office at Princeton University read, "Not everything that counts can be counted, and not everything that can be counted counts." We don't have to wait for more, needed, research to act on common sense, or to give the gift of nature—even when it might seem to be too late.

Touching the Sky with a Stick

On a Sunday afternoon, a half-dozen teenagers gathered in defense attorney Daniel Ybarra's office not far from where I live. These teenagers—several diagnosed with ADHD—were on probation. They looked like your usual troubled teenage suspects: a gang member wearing a white net skullcap and black jersey; a girl with orange hair, her fingernails chewed to the quick; another boy with a black skullcap with a bandana tied around his head. He was wearing a sealskin Tlingit medicine pouch around his neck.

"You gonna carry your bus tokens in that, now?" one of the teens teased.

They had just returned from two chaperoned weeks living with tribal people in Ketchikan, Alaska, and in the southwestern Alaskan village of Kake, population 750. Kake is on an island served by a ferry that comes once every five days. The young people had been ordered to Alaska by a superior court judge who has an interest in alternative approaches to punishment.

For years, Ybarra had dreamed of pulling at-risk kids out of their urban environment and exposing them to nature. With the blessing of the judge, he acted. He persuaded Alaska Airlines to provide inexpensive airline tickets and raised contributions from law school classmates, a professional football player, and the United Domestic Workers union.

Some of the teenagers Ybarra took under his wing had never been to the mountains or beyond earshot of a combustion engine. The farthest one girl had been from her inner city home was a trip to a suburb. Suddenly they were transported to a place of glaciers and *takus*—storms that come out of nowhere, with winds that can blow a forest flat. They found themselves among grizzlies on the beaches, sea elephants that loomed up from the channel, and bald eagles that sat ten to a branch, as common as sparrows.

Tlingit villages face the sea, as they have for thousands of years, and life still revolves around the ocean's harvest. Although the Tlingits have their own problems with substance abuse, they retain pieces of what so many young people have lost. The boy with the black skullcap said: "I never seen a place so dark at night. I seen seals, bears, whales, salmon jumpin'—and I caught crabs and oysters, and as soon as we caught 'em, we ate 'em. I felt like I was in a past life." A girl dressed in neo-hippie garb added: "I never saw a bear before. I'm scared of bears, but when I saw them, I had no stress. I was calm, free. You know what was great? Picking berries. It was addictive. Like cigarettes." She laughed. "Just the picking, just being out in the bushes."

One of the young men said he almost refused to get on the airplane to come home. But he returned determined to become an attorney specializing in environmental law.

They learned about *sba-a-ya-dee-da-na*, a Tlingit word that loosely translates as "self-respect," by being in nature, and by associating with people who had never been separated from it.

"I met a little boy and spent a lot of time with him," said one of the young women in the room. She had long, dark hair and eyes as bright as the midnight sun. "One day I was outside—this was right before we went into a sweat lodge—and he asked me, 'Can you touch the sky with a stick?' I answered, 'No, I'm too short.' He looked at me with disgust and said, 'You're weak! How do you know you can't touch the sky with a stick if you don't even try?'" Recalling the riddle, the young woman's eyes widened. "This was the first time I've ever been spoken to like that by a four-year-old."

When she came home, her mother was not at the airport to pick her up. She returned to an empty house.

"Last night, I looked out at the trees and I thought of Kake," she said.

Anyone who has spent much time around addicts or gang members understands how disarming—and manipulative—they can be. Yet on this afternoon, I saw no evidence of the con artist in their eyes. At least for a while—a day, a week, a year, or perhaps even a lifetime—they were changed.

Excerpt from *Collapse: How Societies Choose to Fail or Succeed*

A Tale of Two Farms

Jared Diamond

A few summers ago I visited two dairy farms, Huls Farm and Gardar Farm, which despite being located thousands of miles apart were still remarkably similar in their strengths and vulnerabilities. Both were by far the largest, most prosperous, most technologically advanced farms in their respective districts. In particular, each was centered around a magnificent state-of-the-art barn for sheltering and milking cows. Those structures, both neatly divided into opposite-facing rows of cow stalls, dwarfed all other barns in the district. Both farms let their cows graze outdoors in lush pastures during the summer, produced their own hay to harvest in the late summer for feeding the cows through the winter, and increased their production of summer fodder and winter hay by irrigating their fields. The two farms were similar in area (a few square miles) and in barn size, Huls barn holding somewhat more cows than Gardar barn (200 vs. 165 cows, respectively). The owners of both farms were viewed as leaders of their respective societies. Both owners were deeply religious. Both farms were located in gorgeous natural settings that attract tourists from afar, with backdrops of high snow-capped mountains drained by streams teaming with fish, and sloping down to a famous river (below Huls Farm) or fjord (below Gardar Farm).

Those were the shared strengths of the two farms. As for their shared vulnerabilities, both lay in districts economically marginal for dairying, because their high northern latitudes meant a short summer growing season in which to produce pasture grass and hay. Because the climate was thus suboptimal even in good years, compared to dairy farms at lower latitudes, both farms were susceptible to being harmed by climate change, with drought or cold being the main concerns in the districts of Huls Farm or Gardar Farm respectively. Both districts lay far from population centers to which they could market their products, so that transportation costs and hazards placed them at a competitive disadvantage compared to more centrally located districts. The economies of both farms were hostage to forces beyond their owners' control, such as the changing affluence and tastes of their customers and neighbors. On a larger scale, the economies of the countries in which both farms lay rose and fell with the waxing and waning of threats from distant enemy societies.

The biggest difference between Huls Farm and Gardar Farm is in their current status. Huls Farm, a family enterprise owned by five siblings and their spouses in the Bitterroot Valley of the western U.S. state of Montana, is currently prospering, while Ravalli County in which Huls Farm lies boasts one of the highest population growth rates of any American county. Tim, Trudy, and Dan Huls, who are among Huls Farm's owners, personally took me on a tour of their high-tech new barn, and patiently explained to me the attractions and vicissitudes of dairy farming in Montana. It is inconceivable that the United States in general, and Huls Farm in particular, will collapse in the foreseeable future. But Gardar Farm, the former manor farm of the Norse bishop of southwestern Greenland, was abandoned over 500 years ago. Greenland Norse society collapsed completely: its thousands of inhabitants starved to death, were killed in civil unrest or in war against an enemy, or emigrated, until nobody remained alive. While the strongly built stone walls of Gardar barn and nearby Gardar Cathedral are still standing, so that I was able to count the individual cow stalls, there is no owner to tell me today of Gardar's former attractions and vicissitudes. Yet when Gardar Farm and Norse Greenland were at their peak, their decline seemed as inconceivable as does the decline of Huls Farm and the U.S. today.

Let me make clear: in drawing these parallels between Huls and Gardar Farms, I am not claiming that Huls Farm and American society are doomed to decline. At present, the truth is quite the opposite: Huls Farm is in the process of expanding, its advanced new technology is being studied for adoption by neighboring farms, and the United States is now the most powerful country in the world. Nor am I claiming that farms or societies in general are prone to collapse: while some have indeed collapsed like Gardar, others have survived uninterruptedly for thousands of years. Instead, my trips to Huls and Gardar Farms, thousands of miles apart but visited during the same summer, vividly brought home to me the conclusion that even the richest, technologically most advanced societies today face growing environmental and economic problems that should not be underestimated. Many of our problems are broadly similar to those that undermined Gardar Farm and Norse Greenland, and that many other past societies also struggled to solve. Some of those past societies failed (like the Greenland Norse), and others succeeded (like the Japanese and Tikopians). The past offers us a rich database from which we can learn, in order that we may keep on succeeding.

Norse Greenland is just one of many past societies that collapsed or vanished, leaving behind monumental ruins such as those that Shelley imagined in his poem "Ozymandias." By collapse, I mean a drastic decrease in human population size and/or political/economic/social complexity, over a considerable area, for an extended time. The phenomenon of collapses is thus an extreme form of several milder types of decline, and it becomes arbitrary to decide how drastic the decline of a society must be before it qualifies to be labeled as a collapse. Some of those milder types of decline include the normal minor rises and falls of fortune,

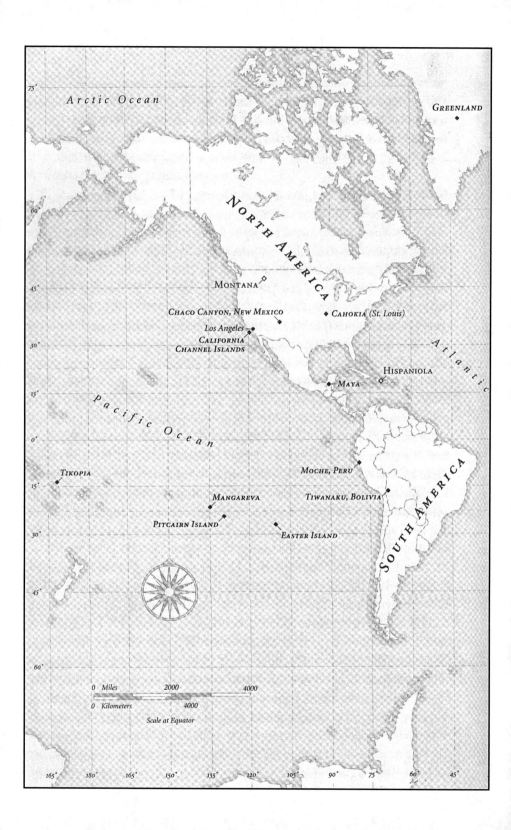

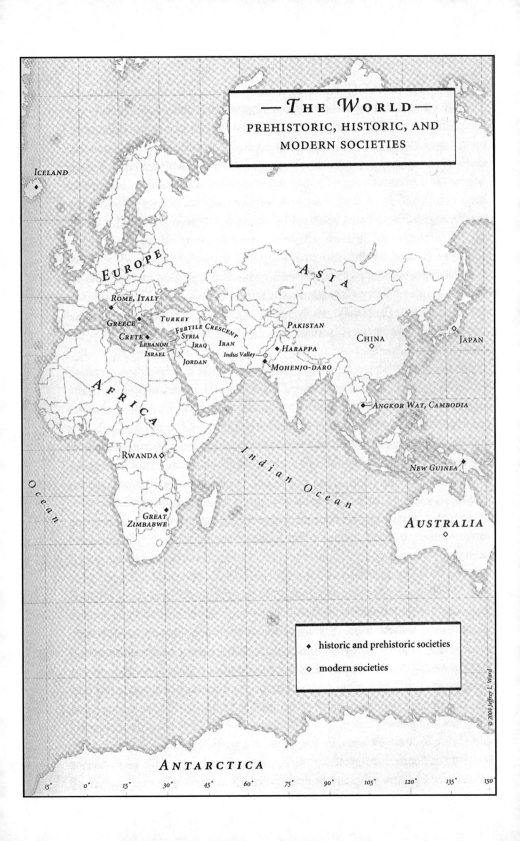

and minor political/economic/social restructurings, of any individual society; one society's conquest by a close neighbor, or its decline linked to the neighbor's rise, without change in the total population size or complexity of the whole region; and the replacement or overthrow of one governing elite by another. By those standards, most people would consider the following past societies to have been famous victims of full-fledged collapses rather than of just minor declines: the Anasazi and Cahokia within the boundaries of the modern U.S., the Maya cities in Central America, Moche and Tiwanaku societies in South America, Mycenean Greece and Minoan Crete in Europe, Great Zimbabwe in Africa, Angkor Wat and the Harappan Indus Valley cities in Asia, and Easter Island in the Pacific Ocean (map, pp. [18–19]).

The monumental ruins left behind by those past societies hold a romantic fascination for all of us. We marvel at them when as children we first learn of them through pictures. When we grow up, many of us plan vacations in order to experience them at firsthand as tourists. We feel drawn to their often spectacular and haunting beauty, and also to the mysteries that they pose. The scales of the ruins testify to the former wealth and power of their builders—they boast "Look on my works, ye mighty, and despair!" in Shelley's words. Yet the builders vanished, abandoning the great structures that they had created at such effort. How could a society that was once so mighty end up collapsing? What were the fates of its individual citizens?—did they move away, and (if so) why, or did they die there in some unpleasant way? Lurking behind this romantic mystery is the nagging thought: might such a fate eventually befall our own wealthy society? Will tourists someday stare mystified at the rusting hulks of New York's skyscrapers, much as we stare today at the jungle-overgrown ruins of Maya cities?

It has long been suspected that many of those mysterious abandonments were at least partly triggered by ecological problems: people inadvertently destroying the environmental resources on which their societies depended. This suspicion of unintended ecological suicide—ecocide—has been confirmed by discoveries made in recent decades by archaeologists, climatologists, historians, paleontologists, and palynologists (pollen scientists). The processes through which past societies have undermined themselves by damaging their environments fall into eight categories, whose relative importance differs from case to case: deforestation and habitat destruction, soil problems (erosion, salinization, and soil fertility losses), water management problems, overhunting, overfishing, effects of introduced species on native species, human population growth, and increased per-capita impact of people.

Those past collapses tended to follow somewhat similar courses constituting variations on a theme. Population growth forced people to adopt intensified means of agricultural production (such as irrigation, double-cropping, or terracing), and to expand farming from the prime lands first chosen onto more marginal land, in order to feed the growing number of hungry mouths. Unsustainable practices led to environmental damage of one or more of the eight types just listed, resulting in agriculturally marginal lands having to be abandoned again. Consequences for society included food shortages, starvation, wars among too many people fighting for too few resources, and overthrows of governing elites by disillusioned masses. Eventually, population decreased through starvation, war, or disease, and society lost some of the political, economic, and cultural complexity that it had developed at its peak. Writers find it tempting to draw analogies between those trajectories of human societies and the trajectories of individual human lives—to talk of a society's birth, growth, peak, senescence, and death—and to assume that the long period of senescence that most of us traverse between our peak years and our deaths also applies to societies. But that metaphor proves erroneous for many past societies (and for the modern Soviet Union): they declined rapidly after reaching peak numbers and power, and those rapid declines must have come as a surprise and shock to their citizens. In the worst cases of complete collapse, everybody in the society emigrated or died. Obviously, though, this grim trajectory is not one that all past societies followed unvaryingly to completion: different societies collapsed to different degrees and in somewhat different ways, while many societies didn't collapse at all.

The risk of such collapses today is now a matter of increasing concern; indeed, collapses have already materialized for Somalia, Rwanda, and some other Third World countries. Many people fear that ecocide has now come to overshadow nuclear war and emerging diseases as a threat to global civilization. The environmental problems facing us today include the same eight that undermined past societies, plus four new ones: human-caused climate change, buildup of toxic chemicals in the environment, energy shortages, and full human utilization of the Earth's photosynthetic capacity. Most of these 12 threats, it is claimed, will become globally critical within the next few decades: either we solve the problems by then, or the problems will undermine not just Somalia but also First World societies. Much more likely than a doomsday scenario involving human extinction or an apocalyptic collapse of industrial civilization would be "just" a future of significantly lower living standards, chronically higher risks, and the undermining of what we now consider some of our key values. Such a collapse could assume various forms, such as the worldwide spread of diseases or else of wars, triggered ultimately by scarcity of environmental resources. If this reasoning is correct, then our efforts today will determine the state of the world in which the current generation of children and young adults lives out their middle and late years.

But the seriousness of these current environmental problems is vigorously debated. Are the risks greatly exaggerated, or conversely are they underestimated? Does it stand to reason that today's human population of almost seven billion, with our potent modern technology, is causing our environment to crumble globally at a much more rapid rate than a mere few million people with stone and wooden tools already made it crumble locally in the past? Will modern technology solve our problems, or is it creating new problems faster than it solves old ones? When we deplete one resource (e.g., wood, oil, or ocean fish), can we count on being able to substitute some new resource (e.g., plastics, wind and solar energy, or farmed fish)? Isn't the rate of human population growth declining, such that we're already on course for the world's population to level off at some manageable number of people?

All of these questions illustrate why those famous collapses of past civilizations have taken on more meaning than just that of a romantic mystery. Perhaps there are some practical lessons that we could learn from all those past collapses. We know that some past societies collapsed while others didn't: what made certain societies especially vulnerable? What, exactly, were the processes by which past societies committed ecocide? Why did some past societies fail to see the messes that they were getting into, and that (one would think in retrospect) must have been obvious? Which were the solutions that succeeded in the past? If we could answer these questions, we might be able to identify which societies are now most at risk, and what measures could best help them, without waiting for more Somalia-like collapses.

But there are also differences between the modern world and its problems, and those past societies and their problems. We shouldn't be so naïve as to think that study of the past will yield simple solutions, directly transferable to our societies today. We differ from past societies in some respects that put us at lower risk than them; some of those respects often mentioned include our powerful technology (i.e., its beneficial effects), globalization, modern medicine, and greater knowledge of past societies and of distant modern societies. We also differ from past societies in some respects that put us at greater risk than them: mentioned in that connection are, again, our potent technology (i.e., its unintended destructive effects), globalization (such that now a collapse even in remote Somalia affects the U.S. and Europe), the dependence of millions (and, soon, billions) of us on modern medicine for our survival, and our much larger human population. Perhaps we can still learn from the past, but only if we think carefully about its lessons.

Efforts to understand past collapses have had to confront one major controversy and four complications. The controversy involves resistance to the idea that past peoples (some of them known to be ancestral to peoples currently alive and vocal) did things that contributed to their own decline. We are much more conscious of environmental damage now than we were a mere few decades ago. Even signs in hotel rooms now invoke love of the environment to make us feel guilty if we demand fresh towels or let the water run. To damage the environment today is considered morally culpable.

Not surprisingly, Native Hawaiians and Maoris don't like paleontologists telling them that their ancestors exterminated half of the bird species that had evolved on Hawaii and New Zealand, nor do Native Americans like archaeologists telling them that the Anasazi deforested parts of the southwestern U.S. The supposed discoveries by paleontologists and archaeologists sound to some listeners like just one more racist pretext advanced by whites for dispossessing indigenous peoples. It's as if scientists were saying, "Your ancestors were bad stewards of their lands, so they deserved to be dispossessed." Some American and Australian whites, resentful of government payments and land retribution to Native Americans and Aboriginal Australians, do indeed seize on the discoveries to advance that argument today. Not only indigenous peoples, but also some anthropologists and archaeologists who study them and identify with them, view the recent supposed discoveries as racist lies.

Some of the indigenous peoples and the anthropologists identifying with them go to the opposite extreme. They insist that past indigenous peoples were (and modern ones still are) gentle and ecologically wise stewards of their environments, intimately knew and respected Nature, innocently lived in a virtual Garden of Eden, and could never have done all those bad things. As a New Guinea hunter once told me, "If one day I succeed in shooting a big pigeon in one direction from our village, I wait a week before hunting pigeons again, and then I go out in the opposite direction from the village." Only those evil modern First World inhabitants are ignorant of Nature, don't respect the environment, and destroy it.

In fact, both extreme sides in this controversy—the racists and the believers in a past Eden—are committing the error of viewing past indigenous peoples as fundamentally different from (whether inferior to or superior to) modern First World peoples. Managing environmental resources sustainably has *always* been difficult, ever since *Homo sapiens* developed modern inventiveness, efficiency, and hunting skills by around 50,000 years ago. Beginning with the first human colonization of the Australian continent around 46,000 years ago, and the subsequent prompt extinction of most of Australia's former giant marsupials and other large animals, every human colonization of a land mass formerly lacking humans—whether of Australia, North America, South America, Madagascar, the Mediterranean islands, or Hawaii and New Zealand and dozens of other Pacific islands—has been followed by a wave of extinction of large animals that had evolved without fear of humans and were easy to kill, or else succumbed to human-associated habitat changes, introduced pest species, and diseases. Any people can fall into the trap of overexploiting environmental resources, because of ubiquitous problems that we shall consider later in this book: that the resources initially seem inexhaustibly abundant; that signs of their incipient depletion become masked by normal fluctuations in resource levels between years or decades; that it's difficult to get people to agree on exercising restraint in harvesting a shared resource (the so-called tragedy of the commons, to be discussed in later chapters); and that the complexity of ecosystems often makes the consequences of some human-caused perturbation virtually impossible to predict even for a professional ecologist. Environmental problems that are hard to manage today were surely even harder to manage in the past. Especially for past non-literate peoples who couldn't read case studies of societal collapses, ecological damage constituted a tragic, unforeseen, unintended consequence of their best efforts, rather than morally culpable blind or conscious selfishness. The societies that ended up collapsing were (like the Maya) among the most creative and (for a time) advanced and successful of their times, rather than stupid and primitive.

Past peoples were neither ignorant bad managers who deserved to be exterminated or dispossessed, nor all-knowing conscientious environmentalists who solved problems that we can't solve today. They were people like us, facing problems broadly similar to those that we now face. They were prone either to succeed or to fail, depending on circumstances similar to those making us prone to succeed or to fail today. Yes, there are differences between the situation we face today and that faced by past peoples, but there are still enough similarities for us to be able to learn from the past.

Above all, it seems to me wrongheaded and dangerous to invoke historical assumptions about environmental practices of native peoples in order to justify treating them fairly. In many or most cases, historians and archaeologists have been uncovering overwhelming evidence that this assumption (about Eden-like environmentalism) is wrong. By invoking this assumption to justify fair treatment of native peoples, we imply that it would be OK to mistreat them if that assumption could be refuted. In fact, the case against mistreating them isn't based on any historical assumption about their environmental practices: it's based on a moral principle, namely, that it is morally wrong for one people to dispossess, subjugate, or exterminate another people.

That's the controversy about past ecological collapses. As for the complications, of course it's not true that all societies are doomed to collapse because of environmental damage: in the past some societies did while others didn't; the real question is why only some societies proved fragile, and what distinguished those that collapsed from those that didn't. Some societies that I shall discuss, such as the Icelanders and Tikopians, succeeded in solving extremely difficult environmental problems, have thereby been able to persist for a long time, and are still going strong today. For example, when Norwegian colonists of

Iceland first encountered an environment superficially similar to that of Norway but in reality very different, they inadvertently destroyed much of Iceland's topsoil and most of its forests. Iceland for a long time was Europe's poorest and most ecologically ravaged country. However, Icelanders eventually learned from experience, adopted rigorous measures of environmental protection, and now enjoy one of the highest per-capita national average incomes in the world. Tikopia Islanders inhabit a tiny island so far from any neighbors that they were forced to become self-sufficient in almost everything, but they micromanaged their resources and regulated their population size so carefully that their island is still productive after 3,000 years of human occupation. Thus, this book is not an uninterrupted series of depressing stories of failure, but also includes success stories inspiring imitation and optimism.

In addition, I don't know of any case in which a society's collapse can be attributed solely to environmental damage: there are always other contributing factors. When I began to plan this book, I didn't appreciate those complications, and I naïvely thought that the book would just be about environmental damage. Eventually, I arrived at a five-point framework of possible contributing factors that I now consider in trying to understand any putative environmental collapse. Four of those sets of factors—environmental damage, climate change, hostile neighbors, and friendly trade partners—may or may not prove significant for a particular society. The fifth set of factors—the society's responses to its environmental problems—always proves significant. Let's consider these five sets of factors one by one, in a sequence not implying any primacy of cause but just convenience of presentation.

A first set of factors involves damage that people inadvertently inflict on their environment, as already discussed. The extent and reversibility of that damage depend partly on properties of people (e.g., how many trees they cut down per acre per year), and partly on properties of the environment (e.g., properties determining how many seedlings germinate per acre, and how rapidly saplings grow, per year). Those environmental properties are referred to either as fragility (susceptibility to damage) or as resilience (potential for recovery from damage), and one can talk separately of the fragility or resilience of an area's forests, its soils, its fish populations, and so on. Hence the reasons why only certain societies suffered environmental collapses might in principle involve either exceptional imprudence of their people, exceptional fragility of some aspects of their environment, or both.

A next consideration in my five-point framework is climate change, a term that today we tend to associate with global warming caused by humans. In fact, climate may become hotter or colder, wetter or drier, or more or less variable between months or between years, because of changes in natural forces that drive climate and that have nothing to do with humans. Examples of such forces include changes in the heat put out by the sun, volcanic eruptions that inject dust into the atmosphere, changes in the orientation of the Earth's axis with respect to its orbit, and changes in the distribution of land and ocean over the face of the Earth. Frequently discussed cases of natural climate change include the advance and retreat of continental ice sheets during the Ice Ages beginning over two million years ago, the so-called Little Ice Age from about A.D. 1400 to 1800, and the global cooling following the enormous volcanic eruption of Indonesia's Mt. Tambora on April 5, 1815. That eruption injected so much dust into the upper atmosphere that the amount of sunlight reaching the ground decreased until the dust settled out, causing widespread famines even in North America and Europe due to cold temperatures and reduced crop yields in the summer of 1816 ("the year without a summer").

Climate change was even more of a problem for past societies with short human lifespans and without writing than it is today, because climate in many parts of the world tends to vary not just from year to year but also on a multi-decade time scale; e.g., several wet decades followed by a dry half-century. In many prehistoric societies the mean human generation time—average number of years between births of parents and of their children—was only a few decades. Hence towards the end of a string of wet decades, most people alive could have had no firsthand memory of the previous period of dry climate. Even today, there is a human tendency to increase production and population during good decades, forgetting (or, in the past, never realizing) that such decades were unlikely to last. When the good decades then do end, the society finds itself with more population than can be supported, or with ingrained habits unsuitable to the new climate conditions. (Just think today of the dry U.S. West and its urban or rural policies of profligate water use, often drawn up in wet decades on the tacit assumption that they were typical.) Compounding these problems of climate change, many past societies didn't have "disaster relief" mechanisms to import food surpluses from other areas with a different climate into areas developing food shortages. All of those considerations exposed past societies to increased risk from climate change.

Natural climate changes may make conditions either better or worse for any particular human society, and may benefit one society while hurting another society. (For example, we shall see that the Little Ice Age was bad for the Greenland Norse but good for the Greenland Inuit.) In many historical cases, a society that was depleting its environmental resources could absorb the losses as long as the climate was benign, but was then driven over the brink of collapse when the climate became drier, colder, hotter, wetter, or more variable. Should one then say that the collapse was caused by human environmental impact, or by climate change? Neither of those simple alternatives is correct. Instead, if the society hadn't already partly depleted its environmental resources, it might have survived the resource depletion caused by climate change. Conversely, it was able to survive its self-inflicted resource depletion until climate change produced further resource depletion. It was neither factor taken alone, but the combination of environmental impact and climate change, that proved fatal.

A third consideration is hostile neighbors. All but a few historical societies have been geographically close enough to some other societies to have had at least some contact with them. Relations with neighboring societies may be intermittently or chronically hostile. A society may be able to hold off its enemies as long as it is strong, only to succumb when it becomes weakened for any reason, including environmental damage. The proximate cause of the collapse will then be military conquest, but the ultimate cause—the factor whose change led to the collapse—will have been the factor that caused the weakening. Hence collapses for ecological or other reasons often masquerade as military defeats.

The most familiar debate about such possible masquerading involves the fall of the Western Roman Empire. Rome became increasingly beset by barbarian invasions, with the conventional date for the Empire's fall being taken somewhat arbitrarily as A.D. 476, the year in which the last emperor of the West was deposed. However, even before the rise of the Roman Empire, there had been "barbarian" tribes who lived in northern Europe and Central Asia beyond the borders of "civilized" Mediterranean Europe, and who periodically attacked civilized Europe (as well as civilized China and India). For over a thousand years, Rome successfully held off the barbarians, for instance slaughtering a large invading force of Cimbri and Teutones bent on conquering northern Italy at the Battle of Campi Raudii in 101 B.C.

Eventually, it was the barbarians rather than Romans who won the battles: what was the fundamental reason for that shift in fortune? Was it because of changes in the barbarians themselves, such that they became more numerous or better organized, acquired better weapons or more horses, or profited from climate change in the Central Asian steppes? In that case, we would say that barbarians really could be identified as the fundamental cause of Rome's fall. Or was it instead that the same old unchanged barbarians were always waiting on the Roman Empire's frontiers, and that they couldn't prevail until Rome became weakened by some combination of economic, political, environmental, and other problems? In that case we would blame Rome's fall on its own problems, with the barbarians just providing the coup de grâce. This question continues to be debated. Essentially the same question has been debated for the fall of the Khmer Empire centered on Angkor Wat in relation to invasions by Thai neighbors, for the decline in Harappan Indus Valley civilization in relation to Aryan invasions, and for the fall of Mycenean Greece and other Bronze Age Mediterranean societies in relation to invasions by Sea Peoples.

The fourth set of factors is the converse of the third set: decreased support by friendly neighbors, as opposed to increased attacks by hostile neighbors. All but a few historical societies have had friendly trade partners as well as neighboring enemies. Often, the partner and the enemy are one and the same neighbor, whose behavior shifts back and forth between friendly and hostile. Most societies depend to some extent on friendly neighbors, either for imports of essential trade goods (like U.S. imports of oil, and Japanese imports of oil, wood, and seafood, today), or else for cultural ties that lend cohesion to the society (such as Australia's cultural identity imported from Britain until recently). Hence the risk arises that, if your trade partner becomes weakened for any reason (including environmental damage) and can no longer supply the essential import or the cultural tie, your own society may become weakened as a result. This is a familiar problem today because of the First World's dependence on oil from ecologically fragile and politically troubled Third World countries that imposed an oil embargo in 1973. Similar problems arose in the past for the Greenland Norse, Pitcairn Islanders, and other societies.

The last set of factors in my five-point framework involves the ubiquitous question of the society's responses to its problems, whether those problems are environmental or not. Different societies respond differently to similar problems. For instance, problems of deforestation arose for many past societies, among which Highland New Guinea, Japan, Tikopia, and Tonga developed successful forest management and continued to prosper, while Easter Island, Mangareva, and Norse Greenland failed to develop successful forest management and collapsed as a result. How can we understand such differing outcomes? A society's responses depend on its political, economic, and social institutions and on its cultural values. Those institutions and values affect whether the society solves (or even tries to solve) its problems. In this book we shall consider this five-point framework for each past society whose collapse or persistence is discussed.

I should add, of course, that just as climate change, hostile neighbors, and trade partners may or may not contribute to a particular society's collapse, environmental damage as well may or may not contribute. It would be absurd to claim that environmental damage must be a major factor in all collapses: the collapse of the Soviet Union is a modern counter-example, and the destruction of Carthage by Rome in 146 B.C. is an ancient one. It's obviously true that military or economic factors alone may suffice. Hence a full title for this book would be "Societal collapses involving an environmental component, and in some cases also contributions of climate change, hostile neighbors, and trade partners, plus questions of societal responses." That restriction still leaves us ample modern and ancient material to consider.

Issues of human environmental impacts today tend to be controversial, and opinions about them tend to fall on a spectrum between two opposite camps. One camp, usually referred to as "environmentalist" or "pro-environment," holds that our current environmental problems are serious and in urgent need of addressing, and that current rates of economic and population growth cannot be sustained. The other camp holds that environmentalists' concerns are exaggerated and unwarranted, and that continued economic and population growth is both possible and desirable. The latter camp isn't associated with an accepted short label, and so I shall refer to it simply as "non-environmentalist." Its adherents come especially from the world of big business and economics, but the equation "non-environmentalist" = "pro-business" is imperfect; many businesspeople consider themselves environmentalists, and many people skeptical of environmentalists' claims are not in the world of big business. In writing this book, where do I stand myself with the respect to these two camps?

On the one hand, I have been a bird-watcher since I was seven years old. I trained professionally as a biologist, and I have been doing research on New Guinea rainforest birds for the past 40 years. I love birds, enjoy watching them, and enjoy being in rainforest. I also like other plants, animals, and habitats and value them for their own sakes. I've been active in many efforts to preserve species and natural environments in New Guinea and elsewhere. For the past dozen years I've been a director of the U.S. affiliate of World Wildlife Fund, one of the largest international environmentalist organizations and the one with the most cosmopolitan interests. All of those things have earned me criticism from non-environmentalists, who use phrases such as "fearmonger," "Diamond preaches gloom and doom," "exaggerates risks," and "favors endangered purple louseworts over the needs of people." But while I do love New Guinea birds, I love much more my sons, my wife, my friends, New Guineans, and other people. I'm more interested in environmental issues because of what I see as their consequences for people than because of their consequences for birds.

On the other hand, I have much experience, interest, and ongoing involvement with big businesses and other forces in our society that exploit environmental resources and are often viewed as anti-environmentalist. As a teenager, I worked on large cattle ranches in Montana, to which, as an adult and father, I now regularly take my wife and my sons for summer vacations. I had a job on a crew of Montana copper miners for one summer. I love Montana and my rancher friends, I understand and admire and sympathize with their agribusinesses and their lifestyles, and I've dedicated this book to them. In recent years I've also had much opportunity to observe and become familiar with other large extractive companies in the mining, logging, fishing, oil, and natural gas industries. For the last seven years I've been monitoring environmental impacts in Papua New Guinea's largest producing oil and natural gas field, where oil companies have engaged World Wildlife Fund to provide independent assessments of the environment. I have often been a guest of extractive businesses on their properties, I've talked a lot with their directors and employees, and I've come to understand their own perspectives and problems.

While these relationships with big businesses have given me close-up views of the devastating environmental damage that they often cause, I've also had close-up views of situations where big businesses found it in their interests to adopt environmental safeguards more draconian and effective than I've encountered even in national parks. I'm interested in what motivates these differing environmental policies of different businesses. My involvement with large oil companies in particular has brought me condemnation from some environmentalists, who use phrases such as "Diamond has sold out to big business," "He's in bed with big businesses," or "He prostitutes himself to the oil companies."

In fact, I am not hired by big businesses, and I describe frankly what I see happening on their properties even though I am visiting as their guest. On some properties I have seen oil companies and logging companies being destructive, and I have said so; on other properties I have seen them being careful, and that was what I said. My view is that, if environmentalists aren't willing to engage with big businesses, which are among the most powerful forces in the modern world, it won't be possible to solve the world's environmental problems. Thus, I am writing this book from a middle-of-the-road perspective, with experience of both environmental problems and of business realities.

How can one study the collapses of societies "scientifically"? Science is often misrepresented as "the body of knowledge acquired by performing replicated controlled experiments in the laboratory." Actually, science is something much broader: the acquisition of reliable knowledge about the world. In some fields, such as chemistry and molecular biology, replicated controlled experiments in the laboratory are feasible and provide by far the most reliable means to acquire knowledge. My formal training was in two such fields of laboratory biology, biochemistry for my undergraduate degree and physiology for my Ph.D. From 1955 to 2002 I conducted experimental laboratory research in physiology, at Harvard University and then at the University of California in Los Angeles.

When I began studying birds in New Guinea rainforest in 1964, I was immediately confronted with the problem of acquiring reliable knowledge without being able to resort to replicated controlled experiments, whether in the laboratory or outdoors. It's usually neither feasible, legal, nor ethical to gain knowledge about birds by experimentally exterminating or manipulating their populations at one site while maintaining their populations at another site as unmanipulated controls. I had to use different methods. Similar methodological problems arise in many other areas of population biology, as well as in astronomy, epidemiology, geology, and paleontology.

A frequent solution is to apply what is termed the "comparative method" or the "natural experiment"—i.e., to compare natural situations differing with respect to the variable of interest. For instance, when I as an ornithologist am interested in effects of New Guinea's Cinnamon-browed Melidectes Honeyeater on populations of other honeyeater species, I compare bird communities on mountains that are fairly similar except that some do and others don't happen to support populations of Cinnamon-browed Melidectes Honeyeaters. Similarly, my books *The Third Chimpanzee: The Evolution and Future of the Human Animal* and *Why Is Sex Fun? The Evolution of Human Sexuality* compared different animal species, especially different species of primates, in an effort to figure out why women (unlike females of most other animal species) undergo menopause and lack obvious signs of ovulation, why men have a relatively large penis (by animal standards), and why humans usually have sex in private (rather than in the open, as almost all other animal species do). There is a large scientific literature on the obvious pitfalls of that comparative method, and on how best to overcome those pitfalls. Especially in historical sciences (like evolutionary biology and historical geology), where it's impossible to manipulate the past experimentally, one has no choice except to renounce laboratory experiments in favor of natural ones.

This book employs the comparative method to understand societal collapses to which environmental problems contribute. My previous book (*Guns, Germs, and Steel: The Fates of Human Societies*) had applied the comparative method to the opposite problem: the differing rates of buildup of human societies on different continents over the last 13,000 years. In the present book focusing instead on collapses rather than on buildups, I compare many past and present societies that differed with respect to environmental fragility; relations with neighbors, political institutions, and other "input" variables postulated to influence a society's stability. The "output" variables that I examine are collapse or survival, and form of the collapse if a collapse does occur. By relating output variables to input variables, I aim to tease out the influence of possible input variables on collapses.

A rigorous, comprehensive, and quantitative application of this method was possible for the problem of deforestation-induced collapses on Pacific islands. Prehistoric Pacific peoples deforested their islands to varying degrees, ranging from only slight to complete deforestation, and with societal outcomes ranging from long-term persistence to complete collapses that left everybody dead. For 81 Pacific islands my colleague Barry Rolett and I graded the extent of deforestation on a numerical scale, and we also graded values of nine input variables (such as rainfall, isolation, and restoration of soil fertility) postulated to influence deforestation. By a statistical analysis we were able to calculate the relative strengths with which each input variable predisposed the outcome to deforestation. Another comparative experiment was possible in the North Atlantic, where medieval Vikings from Norway colonized six islands or land masses differing in suitability for agriculture, ease of trade contact with

Norway, and other input variables, and also differing in outcome (from quick abandonment, to everybody dead after 500 years, to still thriving after 1,200 years). Still other comparisons are possible between societies from different parts of the world.

All of these comparisons rest on detailed information about individual societies, patiently accumulated by archaeologists, historians, and other scholars. At the end of this book I provide references to the many excellent books and papers on the ancient Maya and Anasazi, the modern Rwandans and Chinese, and the other past and present societies that I compare. Those individual studies constitute the indispensable database for my book. But there are additional conclusions that can be drawn from comparisons among those many societies, and that could not have been drawn from detailed study of just a single society. For example, to understand the famous Maya collapse requires not only accurate knowledge of Maya history and the Maya environment; we can place the Maya in a broader context and gain further insights by comparing them with other societies that did or didn't collapse, and that resembled the Maya in some respects and differed from them in other respects. Those further insights require the comparative method.

I have belabored this necessity for both good individual studies and good comparisons, because scholars practicing one approach too often belittle the contributions of the other approach. Specialists in the history of one society tend to dismiss comparisons as superficial, while those who compare tend to dismiss studies of single societies as hopelessly myopic and of limited value for understanding other societies. But we need both types of studies if we are to acquire reliable knowledge. In particular, it would be dangerous to generalize from one society, or even just to be confident about interpreting a single collapse. Only from the weight of evidence provided by a comparative study of many societies with different outcomes can one hope to reach convincing conclusions.

Excerpt from *Tomorrow's Biodiversity*
What Is Biodiversity and Why Is It So Important?

Vandana Shiva

Biodiversity means the diversity of life—the rich diversity of life forms on our beautiful planet. Biodiversity is the very fabric of life—it provides the conditions for life's emergence and maintenance, and the many different ways in which that life is expressed. Biological diversity and cultural diversity are intimately related and interdependent. Biodiversity is in fact the embodiment of centuries of cultural evolution, because humans have co-evolved with other species in the diverse ecosystems of the world. Biodiversity in its turn has shaped the world's diverse cultures. The erosion of biodiversity and the erosion of cultural diversity are related. Both have been threatened by the globalization of an industrial culture based on reductionist knowledge, mechanistic technologies and the commodification of resources.

Throughout the twentieth century it was considered that substitutes could be found for resources supplied by biodiversity: renewable sources of energy—wood and animal energy—could be replaced by fossil fuel; manure for growing food could be replaced by the products of fertilizer factories; and medicines could be made from synthetic molecules. But fossil fuels have given us climate change; agrichemicals have threatened species, undermined soil fertility and human health; and synthetic drugs have had fatal side-effects.

38

People everywhere are looking for alternatives that will conserve our fellow beings and produce sustainable solutions for human health and nutrition. Biodiversity and cultural diversity hold the key to these sustainable alternatives. Around the world organic agriculture is again in favour and on the increase, and alternative medicine, inspired by Chinese, Indian and other indigenous knowledge systems is gaining popularity even in the West.

However, while the movement for the rejuvenation of bio-cultural diversity is growing, new threats are emerging. Economic globalization is rapidly expanding biological and social monocultures, pushing out the diversity that remains. New technologies, such as genetic engineering, are creating new risks of biopollution while increasing chemical pollution.

The destruction of biodiversity translates into the destruction of the diversity of the livelihoods of the large majority of Third World people who make their living as farmers, fishermen, craftspeople and healers. The diversity of life forms is also fast becoming the 'green oil' or raw material for the next industrial revolution based on the emerging biotechnologies. Industry is reorganizing itself as the 'life sciences' industry, changing property laws, environmental laws and trade policies to create markets for genetically engineered products and to establish monopolies in the vital sectors of food and medicine.

Different approaches to scientific knowledge raise fundamentally different problems and give fundamentally different answers to basic questions about the nature of biological organisms, their functions and values, their economic utility, and the impact of genetically engineered organisms on people's health and the environment. Reductionist biology is in conflict with relational biology. The reductionist approach is characterized by the assumption that organisms are mechanical constructs made of genes, their functions are determined by genes and life forms are 'gene machines' that can be redesigned to perform new functions. It provides the basis of genetic engineering and the patenting of life. If organisms are merely bundles of DNA, shuffling

DNA around is like moving bricks around in house construction, or moving machine parts in automobiles.

The Erosion of Biodiversity

At the Earth Summit at Rio de Janeiro in 1992, the Convention on Biological Diversity was drawn up. It provides a comprehensive definition of the term biological diversity, which it defines under Article 2 as: 'The variability among living organisms from all sources including *inter alia*, terrestrial, marine and other aquatic ecosystems and the ecological complexes of which they are a part; this includes diversity within species, between species and ecosystems.' Estimates of the number of species in existence vary from 3.6 million to 100 million, of which, to date, scientists have described an estimated 1.7 million. According to present counts, bacteria have 3,058 recognized species; vascular plants have 260,000; fungi have 70,000; viruses have 500,000; vertebrates have 45,000; and insects have 950,000.

All life forms have an intrinsic worth and a right to evolve freely on their own terms. Humankind is one among millions of other species. It does not have a right to push other species to extinction, or to manipulate them for greed, profit and power without concern for their wellbeing. Compassion for all living things has been the basis of most ancient faiths in the world, and is the basis of contemporary movements for animal welfare, for wilderness protection and for the conservation of biodiversity. Native Americans refer to other species as brothers and sisters. In India we think in terms of the Earth Family.

For agribusiness, the biotechnology industry and the technicians who serve them, however, other species have value only as sources of raw material and profit, and can be manipulated and engineered regardless of their welfare. For instance, cows are just udders for the maximization of milk production using recombinant bovine growth hormones (rbgh). Sheep are 'mammalian bioreactors' for the production of pharmaceuticals in their mammary glands. Microbes and plants are sources of genes and provide substances which can be extracted, recombined with other organisms, patented, and bought and sold in global markets.

The ethical conflict between the intrinsic worth and the commercial value of all life forms has become a major issue in negotiations at the World Trade Organization (WTO), in the commercialization of genetic engineering of plants and animals, and in the patents taken out around the world on plants, animals and microorganisms. In Seattle where the WTO met for trade talks in 1999, in Washington at the World Bank meeting in April 2000, in Davos at the World Economic Forum, and in Millau at José Bové's trial for attacking McDonald's in July 2000, thousands of people took part in protests to call attention to the rights and the inherent value of other species.

Seeing other life forms as biological and genetic raw material is fraught with ecological risks. The smallest microbe plays a critical role in maintaining the ecological processes that create the conditions of life for all species, including, of course, our own. Our ignorance of the ecological functions of diverse forms of life is no excuse for us to push species to extinction, or to manipulate them without concern for the ecological impact. Species now become extinct at the rate of 27,000 per year—1,000 times the natural rate—and human greed and desire for profit are the primary cause of most of these extinctions.

Biodiversity, from genes to species to ecosystems, works in harmony and in concert to create and maintain life. This is at the heart both of ancient wisdom and of new holistic theories, such as James Lovelock's 'Gaia' theory, which is, in summary, that the earth is a living system, self-regulating and self-organizing. Just as our bodies maintain their temperature, the earth's equilibrium is maintained through ecological processes in which biodiversity plays a central role.

Biodiversity is assessed at three fundamental levels of biological organization: genetic, species and ecosystem diversity.

Genetic diversity is the variation at the genetic level, i.e. in the components of nucleic acids which constitute the genetic code. Genes are considered the blueprints of life. While gene theory is elegant for understanding replication and inheritance, it is totally inadequate when extended to a theory of life. Only one per cent of all the genetic material of higher organisms is known to relate to the form and function of the organism. We are still ignorant about the role of the remaining 99 per cent, but, in our usual human arrogance, instead of referring to our 99 per cent ignorance, we refer to the 99 per cent 'junk' DNA. In any case, the complex functions and traits of biological systems cannot be reduced to the genetic level. As the eminent molecular biologist, Professor Richard Strohman of Berkeley, has stated:

> Neither genes nor environments 'cause' complex traits. If a word is needed there, then 'cell' will name the cause. It is the cell, and the body of cells as a whole, that selects from the dynamical interactions inherent in its physical and chemical pathways, and responds formatively and adaptively to the external environment. We have mistakenly replaced the concept and reality of the cell as a dynamical center of integrative activity with the concept of gene causality.
>
> (Interview in *Wild Duck Review,* Summer 1999)

Reducing biodiversity to the genetic level is therefore ecologically and scientifically misguided. The value and functions of living organisms are important at higher levels of organization.

Species diversity is the species richness of an ecosystem—the word species literally means outward or visible form. All cultures have ways of organizing life forms along lines of difference. The ecological significance of species can vary tremendously. A tree of the tropical rainforest can support more than a hundred species of insects, whereas a European alpine plant may have no other species wholly dependent on it.

Ecosystems are ecologically and biologically organized systems consisting of diverse flora and fauna. Since an ecosystem is an ecological unit by definition, a simple arithmetical count of variation is not enough to assess biodiversity. Ecological interactions between diverse species become the key measure for ecosystem diversity. Tropical rainforests are the richest terrestrial ecosystems. They cover 7 per cent of the world's surface area, and may well contain 70 per cent of all species (Groombridge, ed., *Global Biodiversity*, 1992). Oceans occupy two-thirds of the Earth's surface, and, although they are as rich as forest ecosystems, they have been viewed as 'a vast desert, desperately short of nutrients and with living things spread most thinly through them' (Colinvaux, *Why Big Fierce Animals are Rare*, 1980).

For the first 2 billion years of the 3.5 billion years or more that life has existed, bacteria and other microorganisms were the only living things on earth. As the famous geneticist David Suzuki says in *From Naked Ape to Super Species* (1999), 'We owe practically all life to bacteria.' Microorganisms create the planet's living environment which supports life. According to James Lovelock, photosynthetic cyanobacteria were instrumental in producing oxygen, without which human life would not be possible. Microorganisms continue to play a critical role in maintaining biogeochemical cycles. The recycling of water, oxygen, methane, carbon dioxide, nitrogen, sulphur and carbon is made possible by diverse species working incessantly to maintain the ecological processes that support life. Forty per cent of the carbon fixed by photosynthesis is carried out by algae and cyanobacteria in the seas and oceans. Fungi that decay wood release about 85 billion tonnes of carbon as CO_2 into the atmosphere each year. Each year, bacteria fix 240 million tonnes of nitrogen, release 210 million tonnes of nitrogen by denutrification and release 75 million tonnes of ammonia (Groombridge (ed.), *Global Biodiversity*, 1992). The work of micro-organisms reduces industrial activity to insignificance.

The greatest biomass in soil, on the basis of current evidence, is that of the microorganisms, above all the fungi. Soil microorganisms maintain soil structure, contribute to the biodegradation of dead plants and animals, and fix nitrogen, and so are the key to soil fertility. Their destruction by chemicals threatens our survival and our food security. When scientists in Denmark scooped up a cubic metre (35 cubic feet) of earth from a beech forest and took it into their laboratory, they found 50,000 small earthworms, 50,000 insects and mites, and

12 million roundworms. A gram of the same soil revealed 30,000 protozoa, 50,000 algae, 400,000 fungi and billions of individual bacteria of 4,000 unknown species.

Bacteria, fungi and protozoa in the guts of animals perform crucial functions in digestion, without which the so-called higher animals could not exist. Microorganisms are also powerful factors in disease and death.

In the oceans, which are so central to the maintenance of Gaia's life, up to 80 per cent of the biomass and productivity in open waters is contributed by ultra planktonic algae (Anderson, 'The Diversity of Eukaryotic Algae', in *Global Biodiversity*, 1992).

Human beings are clearly highly ignorant of other members of the Earth Family and, at least in the Western worldview, have thought of themselves as sitting on top of a biodiversity pyramid or tree rather than forming a part of a complex web of life. Even the most popular conservation programmes have focused on the species closest to human beings, the large mammals: 'Project Tiger' and 'Project Elephant' have been the dominant models for biodiversity conservation. Microbes have had no conservation movements or campaigns for 'microbe rights' for their protection. Nor has it been recognized that in the final analysis microbes are more powerful than 'Man'.

The lesson from biodiversity is co-operation, not competition. It is that the big depends on the small, and cannot survive by exterminating the small.

Since ecological stability or instability is linked to species interactions, it is the relational approach to biodiversity that is important, not the arithmetical approach. For the same reason, conserving biodiversity cannot be achieved by putting it in a museum or a zoo. Biodiversity in balance creates the conditions of life, and species in conflict and out of balance become life-threatening.

I therefore follow the approach to biodiversity which is based not on the number of species or their variation, but takes account of the ecological web of life that species create in interaction. I differentiate between the arithmetical approach and the ecological approach. The arithmetical approach is currently the dominant one. It relates to 'variation or differences among some set of entities'— and 'number, variety and variability used to describe the number, variety and variability of living organisms' (Groombridge, ed., *Global Biodiversity*, 1992). The extinction of a species means not just the loss of that particular species, but also a threat to the other species that are supported by it through ecological processes. When one plant becomes extinct, with it disappear the twenty to forty animal and insect species that rely on it. Salmon, which spend their adult lives at sea, return to their natal streams to spawn. Bears, eagles and wolves catch the salmon and transfer the nutrients to the land. Marine carbon and nitrogen isotopes in salmon have been tracked by scientists, and 25–40 per cent of the carbon and nitrogen in juvenile salmon was found to come from their parents. Ninety per cent of the nitrogen and carbon in the bodies of grizzly bear was of marine origin. A single bear will catch 750 salmon, of which the partially consumed carcasses become nutrients for trees. Salmon are the biggest source of nitrogen fertilizer for the forest thousands of miles from the ocean. The growth of trees is correlated to the marine carbon and nitrogen the salmon bring to the forest. As David Suzuki says in giving this beautiful example of the web of life, 'The fish need the forest, the forest needs the fish' (*From Naked Ape to Super Species*). This interrelationship and mutual dependence is the reason why biodiversity cannot be looked at in a fragmented, atomized context.

Mass extinctions have taken place during geological time, but the erosion of biodiversity has become a systemic product of industrialization. For animals, habitat loss, caused by large dams, industrial plantations, highways and the expansion of human settlements, is the major threat to species survival. Species of birds and fish have also been pushed to extinction by the use of pesticides; this was the story of Rachel Carson's *Silent Spring* (1965). In 1998, the British Trust for Ornithology (BTO) published a major review of the conservation status of breeding birds since 1992. Twenty species were placed on the BTO's 'high alert' list owing to severe population declines of over 50 per cent in the last twenty-five years (Crick, et al., *Breeding Birds it the Wider Countryside*). A press release of 21 March 1999 by the Royal Society for the Protection of Birds (RSPB) stated that three-quarters of the UK's skylarks—that is 4.6 million—have vanished as a consequence of pesticide use.

According to the International Union for the Conservation of Nature (IUCN), 1,029 birds, 1,083 insects, 507 mammals, 169 reptiles, 57 amphibians, 713 fish, 409 molluscs, 154 corals and sponges, 139 annelid worms and 126 crustaceans are threatened. In terms of percentages, 11.7 percent of the mammal species, 10 percent of the birds, 3.67 per cent of the fish and 3.5 per cent of the reptiles are threatened.

Globalization has accelerated the destruction of biodiversity to such a pace and on such a scale that plants and animals that were common a few years ago have disappeared. Global market integration converts millions of acres of forests and farms into industrial monocultures, displacing and destroying both biodiversity and the cultural diversity of local communities.

According to the dominant paradigm of production, diversity goes against productivity, which creates an imperative for uniformity and monocultures. The irony of modern plant- and animal-breeding is that it destroys the very building blocks on which the technology depends. Forestry development schemes introduce monocultures of industrial species, such as eucalyptus, and push into extinction the diversity of local species that fulfils local needs. The Leipzig Global Plan of Action on Plant Genetic Resources for Food and Agriculture, 1995, based on 158 country reports and 12 regional and sub-regional papers, stated that the chief contemporary cause of the loss of genetic diversity has been the spread of modern, commercial agriculture. Agricultural modernization schemes introduce new and uniform crops into farmers' fields and destroy the diversity of local varieties. In the words of Professor Garrison Wilkes of the University of Massachusetts, this is analogous to taking stones from the foundation of a building in order to repair the roof. Monocultures are ecologically unstable—this alone should be enough to prevent them being viewed as essential to production. The narrowing of the genetic base of agriculture leads to increased vulnerability of production and a threat to food security. Growing uniformity is increasing the risk of crop failure. The imperative to destroy diversity in order to increase productivity comes from a one-dimensional monoculture paradigm which fails to take the diverse functions of diverse species into account. Some of these functions include ecosystem maintenance. Destruction of diversity encourages pests and diseases. More than 70,000 pest species destroy 40 per cent of the world's harvest. During the past forty years, crop loss to insects alone has nearly doubled, despite a tenfold increase in the amount of pesticides applied (Pimental, et al., in *Bio-Science*, December 1997).

Biodiversity has rescued our food security from the risks of genetic uniformity. Wheat breeders used *T. monococcum*, macaroni wheat, for its resistance to rust, caused by *Puccima fungi*. Rust epidemics can destroy 75 per cent of the crop, and even in normal years it causes losses of 4 per cent or 2.3 million tonnes (Prescott-Allen, *Genes from the Wild*, 1983). During the 1970s, grassy stunt virus destroyed more than 116,000 hectares (290 acres) of rice in Indonesia, India, Sri Lanka, Vietnam and the Philippines. It is controlled by introducing resistance from the wild rice species *Oryza nivara*. If this wild rice had not been collected and saved in India, the food security of millions would have been threatened. Of the 6,000 varieties screened, only the wild rice from India had resistance to the disease. Similarly, wild maize varieties have the potential of saving $50–250 million dollars' worth of the maize crop in the USA from disease.

The potato famine in Ireland in 1845–46 was caused by genetic uniformity which led to an epidemic of potato blight, caused by the fungus *Phyto plithora infestans*. The famine reduced Ireland's population from 8.2 million in 1841 to 6.2 million in 1851. Future potato famines were prevented by wild potato varieties from the Andes. Traditional cultures have conserved biodiversity, and this is why it is still available for the rescue of industrial monocultures each time they became vulnerable to disease and pests.

A 1972 National Academy of Sciences study, 'The Genetic Vulnerability of Major Crops', stated: 'The corn crop fell victim to the epidemic because of a quirk in the technology that had designed the corn plants of America, until, in one sense, they had become as alike as identical twins. Whatever made one plant susceptible made them all susceptible.' (Doyle, *Altered Harvest*, 1985.)

As the food industry becomes more concentrated and integrated, uniformity is the result, and the globalization of consumption patterns, by creating monocultures and destroying diversity, has a devastating effect on the poorest on the planet. First, they are pushed into deeper poverty by being forced to 'compete' with globally powerful forces to gain access to the local biological resources. Secondly, their economic alternatives outside the global market are destroyed.

A US Department of Agriculture list of recommended fruits published in 1897 included more than 275 different varieties of apples. Today the apple varieties sold are less than a dozen. Supermarkets around the world essentially offer three types of apples: a red one, the Starking, from the USA; a yellow one, the so-called Golden Delicious, also from the USA; and a green one, the Granny Smith or pippin, from Australia (Vellvé, *Saving the Seed*, 1992). A survey in France showed that a few years ago, the diet was rich with 250 plant species including vegetables, fruits and condiments. Today, barely 60 are cultivated in that country, and of these only 30 make up the bulk of local consumption. Crop genetic resources are disappearing at the rate of 1–2 per cent per annum (UN Food and Agriculture Organization, FAO, Development Education Exchange Papers, September 1993). About 75 per cent of the diversity of agricultural crops is estimated to have been lost since the beginning of the century.

Globally, domestic livestock breeds are disappearing at an annual rate of 5 per cent or 6 breeds per month (FAO, World Watch List for

Domestic Animal Diversity, 5 December 1995). Of 4,000–5,000 breeds, 1,500 are threatened with extinction.

There is considerable evidence globally that the trend is towards monoculture and uniformity and away from diversity:

- In the European Union:
  75 per cent of the milk is produced by a quarter of the dairy farms; 80 per cent of the pork comes from 10 per cent of the pig farms;
  90 per cent of the poultry comes from 10 per cent of the poultry farms;
  60 per cent of the cereals come from 6 per cent of the arable farms.
- In Europe 80 per cent of all farmland is sown to just four crops.
- In the Netherlands:
  a single potato variety covers 80 per cent of potato-growing land;
  three wheat varieties cover 90 per cent of wheat-growing land.
- In the UK:
  three varieties of potatoes make up 68 per cent of the crop;
  one variety makes up the remaining 32 per cent.
- In Greece, wheat diversity has declined by 95 per cent.
- In India, under the impact of the Green Revolution, rice varieties cultivated decreased from more than 100,000 to 10.
- In Sri Lanka, 2,000 varieties of rice were cultivated in 1959, but only 5 major varieties today.
- In India, 50 per cent of the goat breeds, 20 per cent of the cattle breeds and 30 per cent of the sheep breeds are in a danger of disappearing.
- The entire pork economy of the world is based on 4 breeds. In China 40 to 50 breeds were once farmed, and are now being replaced by hybrid pigs bred from the 4 'global' breeds.
- The world's main fishing grounds are being fished beyond their limits. About 70 per cent of the world's conventional marine species are threatened.

- One-fifth of all freshwater fish species known in the 1970s are already extinct or endangered.

The Wealth of the Poor

Biodiversity is not just a conservation issue, it is an issue affecting economic survival. Biodiversity is the means of livelihood and the 'means of production' of the poor who have no access to other assets or means of production. For food and medicine, for energy and fibre, for ceremony and crafts the poor depend on the wealth of biological resources and on their knowledge and skills related to biodiversity. As biodiversity disappears, the poor are further impoverished and deprived of the healthcare and nutrition that biodiversity provides. The consumption patterns of the rich and the production patterns of the powerful can undermine the consumption patterns of the poor by contributing to the erosion of biodiversity.

Agricultural biodiversity is the basis of economic life for two-thirds of the world's population—those people who live in rural economies in the Third World. The diversity of crop varieties and animal breeds have been developed as a response to the diversity of different ecosystems. Rice varieties have been developed to grow in flooded regions and in rainfed mountain slopes. Cattle breeds have been developed to match the climate in deserts and in wet rainforest regions.

There exists a very intricate relationship between local communities and biological diversity. Hunting-and-gathering communities use thousands of plants and animals for food, medicine and shelter. Pastoral, peasant and fishing communities have also developed the knowledge and skills to obtain a sustainable livelihood from living diversity, in both wild and domesticated forms, on the land, in the rivers, lakes and seas. The life of communities has been enhanced spiritually, culturally and economically as the communities in turn have enriched Earth's biodiversity.

All our food comes from wild species that have been domesticated and which need to return to their wild relatives to build genetic resistance to disease and pests. Approximately 80,000 edible plants have been used at one time or another since the beginning of agriculture, of which at least 3,000 have been used consistently. However, only about 150 have been cultivated. Globally we now rely on just eight crops to provide 75 per cent of the world's food.

India is rich in livestock. Breeds adapted to their specific local environmental and climatic conditions are indispensable to the rural economies of their regions. The animals provide draught power and transportation, dung as fertilizer and as cooking fuel, dairy products, wool, meat and leather. There are 26 breeds of cattle in India. The Ongole breed from Andhra Pradesh, excellent milkers, are also very strong, appropriate for heavy ploughing. The Desi from the same region, are hardy and disease-resistant, like the famous Vechur breed of Kerala, now on the brink of extinction. The Nagauri of the north are one of the most useful draught breeds in India, and the Red Sindhi cattle of Rajasthan are both good draught animals and sound milk producers. Rajasthan also possesses several breeds of camel, and of its eight breeds of sheep— six from the desert areas—the Nagra is the best wool producer. Sheep play a vital role in the rural economy providing wool, milk and meat. Tragically, many breeds are faced with extinction following a dramatic decline in their numbers over the last decades.

Over centuries, a delicate equilibrium has evolved between the indigenous animals and the flora of each region. The communities and their livestock are dependent on the wide range of fodder, and each species consumes different plants and trees so that a balance is sustained. A comprehensive medicinal knowledge of local plants has also developed to cure diseases in animals.

It has been estimated that three billion people—60 per cent of the world's population—depend on traditional medicines as a principle source of cures for disease. In India and China, 80–90 per cent of traditional medicines are plant-based, and Chinese herbal treatments alone use 5,000 species. In Kenya, 40 per cent of herbal medicines come from the native forest trees. In Amazonia, an ethnobotanical team has catalogued more than 1,000 plants used by the Indian tribes, many of them as medicine. In South Africa, there are approximately 200,000 traditional healers. In total, about 3,000 species of higher plants are used for traditional medicines and of these about 300 are the most commonly used.

India has a rich and ancient heritage of medical knowledge based on its vast resources of medicinal plant biodiversity. India's medical system is called Ayurveda. Its earliest documentation is found in Aatharvaveda, one of the foremost ancient books of Indian knowledge, wisdom and culture, supposed to date from around 1500 BCE. These systems of knowledge and the sources from which they have evolved have survived millennia because they are built on sustainability. Even today, over 70 per cent of the health needs of India are met by these systems. According to an ethnobotanical survey, there are 7,500 species of plants used for medicinal purposes by local Indian communities.

India has something like 1,400 plants documented in various Ayurvedic texts, approximately 342 in Unani, and close to 328 in the Siddha system. This biodiversity-based traditional medicinal system is still being kept alive by 360,740 Ayurveda practitioners, 29,701 Unani experts and 11,644 specialists of Siddha, not to mention millions of housewives and elders who prepare homemade remedies for common ailments.

Everywhere local people have made independent appraisals of their local resources. The plant *Ephedra vulgaris*, which is found in trans-Himalaya, possesses broncho-dilation properties and is only found in that ecosystem. It is commonly used by the local people as a herbal tea, and taken several times a day. In Ayurveda (unlike most folk traditions, it is not oral but written down) there is a body of knowledge called *dhravya guna shastra*, which is the indigenous knowledge of pharmacology. Since the Vedic period a plant named tulsi (*Ocimum sanctum L.*) has had a very sacred place in Indian healing. In both Ayurveda and Siddha the tulsi leaves and the juices from its leaves, roots and seeds are used to cure various ailments, such as intestinal gas, coughs, worms, skin diseases and kidney disorders. It also regulates the flow of urine, subdues inflammation and restores the body by cleansing the system of toxins, while strengthening and toning every organ.

The Kani tribe of the Agastyar hills in Southern Kerala have a habit of eating the raw leaves of a plant known as arogya pacha (*Trichopus zeylnicus*), which they call 'health drug'. In the Central Himalayas, millet grain cooked in water is mixed with buttermilk and used in the treatment of chickenpox.

Quinine, digitalis and morphine are derived from plants, and even in the USA 40 per cent of all prescriptions still depend on natural sources. The first birth-control pills were made from a plant called *Diascorea*. Digitalis, the most popular medicine for heart problems, is made from *Digitalis* (foxglove) which contains glycosides, which regulate heart beats, in its leaves. Hypertension is treated by reserpine, derived from *Rauwolfia serpentia* which has been used in India for centuries. Quinine, for malaria, is basically an indigenous medicine from Peru. The tree was called quinaol quina-quina by the native Indians. From the rosy periwinkle, *Vinca rosea*, are extracted the cancer cures Vinblastine and Vincristine, and alkaloids derived from *Vinca rosea* are used for Hodgkin's disease and childhood leukemia (Koopowitz and Kaye, *Plant Extinction*, 1990).

It is estimated that 100 million of the world's poorest people depend on fishing for all or part of their livelihoods. According to an estimate by the FAO (UN Food and Agriculture Organization), there are a million large fishing boats and 2 million small boats. Most of the large fishing vessels are controlled by transnational corporations and use all the latest aids to fish-detection, catching and processing, allowing them to become more efficient hunting machines, and so leading to the problem of overfishing. As a special issue of the *Ecologist* reports, completely automatic trawlnets that detect the approach of a school of fish electronically, and automatically pay out or retrieve warp to place the net in the path of the shoal are now appearing on the market. The 'Gloria' super trawlnet, developed in Ireland, measures 110 by 170 metres (360 by 560 feet) at its mouth, large enough to swallow a dozen Boeing jumbo jets. The reduction of all value to commercial value results in the development of technologies which are ecologically crude. Large catches are made possible by the destruction of livelihoods and of diverse species. As a Malaysian community has said:

> The trawlers approved by the government 10 to 15 years ago are strongly opposed by the small inshore fishermen whose income is small and who use traditional nets. We should be concerned with the government's policy of too much dependence on modern science and technology . . . The root cause of the present scarcity of fish is trawler fishing. The trawler overturns the soil on the seabed and scoops up all the small fish and fry.

In India, ever since shrimp became an export commodity through export-oriented fisheries development, there is less to catch and less to eat. Until the end of the 1950s, the marine fish harvest increased at a rate of 5 per cent per annum. By the mid-'80s, after 'development', the rate of growth of the marine fish harvest had decreased. Fish consumption declined in India from 19 kg (42 lbs) per year *per capita* to 9 kg (20 lbs) per year.

From the early 1970s, landings of most of the major seabottom-dwelling fish began to decline sharply, largely because of excessive fishing (in the case of purseining) and destructive fishing (in the case of trawling which degraded the seabed). Catches of sardines and mackerel, once the mainstay of the fisheries, fell from 250,000 tonnes in 1968 to 87,000 tonnes in 1990. In this period in South America the consumption of fish went down by 7.9 per cent and in Africa by 2.9 cent, while European fish consumption rose by 23 per cent.

This is the reason that small fishermen worldwide have organized as the World Forum of Fish Workers to protest for their right to fish. On 23 and 24 November 1994, a million fish workers from nine maritime states in India covering a coastline of over 7,500 kilometres (4,660 miles) went on strike. They were protesting against Indian government policies that gave international joint ventures free access to fish in the country's Exclusive Economic Zone (EEZ). During the week of the National Strike, one joint-venture vessel called at the port in Cochin, Kerala. Its hold contained 2,000 tonnes of perch and snapper, equivalent to the amount caught in one year by 1,000 hook-and-line fishermen in the region.

All the needs of two-thirds of the world's people are met by biodiversity. If biodiversity is reduced, they are poorer. Even the privileged one-third of humanity living in the industrialized world depends on biodiversity. Oil and coal were made by creatures living millions of years ago. The cement that builds giant skyscrapers, bridges and parking lots comes from limestone, the remains of skeletons and shells, corals and other marine life.

While industrial civilization uses the gifts of biodiversity, it abuses the living richness of our world. The CO_2 pumped out by our energy and transportation systems is destabilizing climates, leading to an increase in forest fires, droughts, hurricanes, floods, and a rise in sea levels and sea temperature—all of which contribute to the loss of biodiversity. Industrial agriculture, forestry and fisheries convert rich, diverse ecosystems into biologically impoverished chemically intensive monocultures, writing a death sentence for millions of species while claiming higher 'growth'.

This is at the heart of the present conflicts over biodiversity. Systems that destroy biodiversity and those that conserve it both need it. In biodiversity-based economies it is the growth of biodiversity that is the measure of progress. In biodiversity-annihilating economies, it is the growth of money that is the measure of progress. We could, in fact, talk of systems that are life-centred and biodiversity-centred versus systems that are money- and capital-centred.

Rich and Poor in Biodiversity

When assessed in terms of biodiversity rather than financial capital, the South is rich and the North is poor. The wealth of Europe in the colonial era was, to a large extent, based on the transfer of biological resources from the colonies to the centres of imperial power, and the displacement of local biodiversity in the colonies by monocultures of raw material for

European industry. The historian A. W. Crosby has called the biological transfer of wealth from the Americas to Europe the 'Columbian exchange', because with Columbus's arrival in America began the mass transfer of maize, potatoes, squash, tomatoes, peanuts, common beans, sunflowers and other crops across the Atlantic. Sugar, bananas, coffee, tea, rubber, indigo, cotton and other industrial crops were grown in new sites under the control of newly emerging colonial powers and their state-backed trading companies. The North accumulated wealth by gaining control over the biological resources of the South. Destroying the biodiversity that it could not use or control was the other less visible side of this process of colonization.

In spite of the immeasurable contribution that Third World biodiversity has made to the wealth of industrialized countries, corporations, governments and aid agencies of the North continue to create legal and political frameworks to make the Third World pay for what it originally gave. The emerging trends in global trade and technology work inherently against justice and ecological sustainability. They threaten to create a new era of bio-imperialism, built on the biological impoverishment of the Third World and the biosphere. Patents, industrialization of food and agriculture, globalization of trade through the rules of WTO are the new mechanisms by which the biological wealth of the South is being transferred to the North, leaving the Third World poorer both ecologically and economically.

The Empty Earth Syndrome

Third World countries located in the tropics have been endowed with great biological wealth and are the cradle of biodiversity. This wealth is being rapidly destroyed. In my view there are two root causes. The first arises from the 'empty-earth' paradigm of colonization, which assumes that ecosystems are empty if not taken over by Western industrial man or his clones. For five hundred years, colonization has been based on the idea of the 'emptiness' of the earth and of other cultures. The assumption of the empty land leads to the denial of prior inhabitants and their prior rights. The idea of emptiness also leads to the notion of limitlessness—that there are no limits set by nature or other cultures to be respected, no ecological or ethical limits, no limits to the level of greed or accumulation. The empty-earth hypothesis in addition creates a divided world—divisions which exist and deepen even in globalization, and were evident in the failed round of the WTO talks in Seattle. 'To us they cannot come, our land is full; to them we may go, their land is empty.' (Robert Cushman 1621, quoted in Kadir, *Columbus and the Ends of the Earth*, 1992.) Creating clones of Western forms of industrial production and excessive consumption is called 'development' but is actually 'maldevelopment'. (Shiva, *Staying Alive: Women, Ecology and Development*, 1998.) This view threatens other species and other cultures to extinction because it is blind to their existence, their rights and to the impact of the colonizing culture.

The second cause is what I have described as the monoculture of the mind: the idea that the world is or should be uniform and one-dimensional, that diversity is either disease or deficiency, and monocultures are necessary for the production of more food and economic benefits (Shiva, *Monocultures of the Mind*, 1993). It is the scientific and technological reflection of the empty-earth worldview. The shutting out of alternative ways of knowing and making leads to the assumption that the dominant knowledge and techniques are the only option. This monoculture of the mind destroys biodiversity by blocking the perception of the multiple benefits and uses of biodiversity.

Excerpt from *A Sand County Almanac*
The Land Ethic

Aldo Leopold

When God-like Odysseus returned from the wars in Troy, he hanged all on one rope a dozen slave-girls of his household whom he suspected of misbehavior during his absence.

This hanging involved no question of propriety. The girls were property. The disposal of property was then, as now, a matter of expediency, not of right and wrong.

Concepts of right and wrong were not lacking from Odysseus' Greece: witness the fidelity of his wife through the long years before at last his black-prowed galleys clove the wine-dark seas for home. The ethical structure of that day covered wives, but had not yet been extended to human chattels. During the three thousand years which have since elapsed, ethical criteria have been extended to many fields of conduct, with corresponding shrinkages in those judged by expediency only.

This extension of ethics, so far studied only by philosophers, is actually a process in ecological evolution. Its sequences may be described in ecological as well as in philosophical terms. An ethic, ecologically, is a limitation on freedom of action in the struggle for existence. An ethic, philosophically, is a differentiation of social from anti-social conduct. These are two definitions of one thing. The thing has its origin in the tendency of interdependent individuals or groups to evolve modes of co-operation. The ecologist calls these symbioses. Politics and economics are advanced symbioses in which the original free-for-all competition has been replaced, in part, by co-operative mechanisms with an ethical content.

The complexity of co-operative mechanisms has increased with population density, and with the efficiency of tools. It was simpler, for example, to define the anti-social uses of sticks and stones in the days of the mastodons than of bullets and billboards in the age of motors.

The first ethics dealt with the relation between individuals; the Mosaic Decalogue is an example. Later accretions dealt with the relation between the individual and society. The Golden Rule tries to integrate the individual to society; democracy to integrate social organization to the individual.

There is as yet no ethic dealing with man's relation to land and to the animals and plants which grow upon it. Land, like Odysseus' slave-girls, is still property. The land-relation is still strictly economic, entailing privileges but not obligations.

The extension of ethics to this third element in human environment is, if I read the evidence correctly, an evolutionary possibility and an ecological necessity. It is the third step in a sequence. The first two have already been taken. Individual thinkers since the days of Ezekiel and Isaiah have asserted that the despoliation of land is not only inexpedient but wrong. Society, however, has not yet affirmed their belief. I regard the present conservation movement as the embryo of such an affirmation.

An ethic may be regarded as a mode of guidance for meeting ecological situations so new or intricate, or involving such deferred reactions, that the path of social expediency is not discernible to the average individual. Animal instincts are modes of guidance for the individual in meeting such situations. Ethics are possibly a kind of community instinct in-the-making.

The Community Concept

All ethics so far evolved rest upon a single premise: that the individual is a member of a community of interdependent parts. His instincts prompt him to compete for his place in the community, but his ethics prompt him also to co-operate (perhaps in order that there may be a place to compete for).

The land ethic simply enlarges the boundaries of the community to include soils, waters, plants, and animals, or collectively: the land.

This sounds simple: do we not already sing our love for and obligation to the land of the free and the home of the brave? Yes, but just what and whom do we love? Certainly not the soil, which we are sending helter-skelter downriver. Certainly not the waters, which we assume have no function except to turn turbines, float barges, and carry off sewage. Certainly not the plants, of which we exterminate whole communities without batting an eye. Certainly not the animals, of which we have already extirpated many of the largest and most beautiful species. A land ethic of course cannot prevent the alteration, management, and use of these 'resources,' but it does affirm their right to continued existence, and, at least in spots, their continued existence in a natural state.

In short, a land ethic changes the role of *Homo sapiens* from conqueror of the land-community to plain member and citizen of it. It implies respect for his fellow-members, and also respect for the community as such.

In human history, we have learned (I hope) that the conqueror role is eventually self-defeating. Why? Because it is implicit in such a role that the conqueror knows, *ex cathedra*, just what makes the community clock tick, and just what and who is valuable, and what and who is worthless, in community life. It always turns out that he knows neither, and this is why his conquests eventually defeat themselves.

In the biotic community, a parallel situation exists. Abraham knew exactly what the land was for: it was to drip milk and honey into Abraham's mouth. At the present moment, the assurance with which we regard this assumption is inverse to the degree of our education.

The ordinary citizen today assumes that science knows what makes the community clock tick; the scientist is equally sure that he does not.

He knows that the biotic mechanism is so complex that its workings may never be fully understood.

That man is, in fact, only a member of a biotic team is shown by an ecological interpretation of history. Many historical events, hitherto explained solely in terms of human enterprise, were actually biotic interactions between people and land. The characteristics of the land determined the facts quite as potently as the characteristics of the men who lived on it.

Consider, for example, the settlement of the Mississippi valley. In the years following the Revolution, three groups were contending for its control: the native Indian, the French and English traders, and the American settlers. Historians wonder what would have happened if the English at Detroit had thrown a little more weight into the Indian side of those tipsy scales which decided the outcome of the colonial migration into the cane-lands of Kentucky. It is time now to ponder the fact that the cane-lands, when subjected to the particular mixture of forces represented by the cow, plow, fire, and axe of the pioneer, became bluegrass. What if the plant succession inherent in this dark and bloody ground had, under the impact of these forces, given us some worthless sedge, shrub, or weed? Would Boone and Kenton have held out? Would there have been any overflow into Ohio, Indiana, Illinois, and Missouri? Any Louisiana Purchase? Any transcontinental union of new states? Any Civil War?

Kentucky was one sentence in the drama of history. We are commonly told what the human actors in this drama tried to do, but we are seldom told that their success, or the lack of it, hung in large degree on the reaction of particular soils to the impact of the particular forces exerted by their occupancy. In the case of Kentucky, we do not even know where the bluegrass came from—whether it is a native species, or a stowaway from Europe.

Contrast the cane-lands with what hindsight tells us about the Southwest, where the pioneers were equally brave, resourceful, and persevering. The impact of occupancy here brought no bluegrass, or other plant fitted to withstand the bumps and buffetings of hard use. This region, when grazed by livestock, reverted through a series of more and more worthless grasses, shrubs, and weeds to a condition of unstable equilibrium. Each recession of plant types bred erosion; each increment to erosion bred a further recession of plants. The result today is a progressive and mutual deterioration, not only of plants and soils, but of the animal community subsisting thereon. The early settlers did not expect this: on the ciénegas of New Mexico some even cut ditches to hasten it. So subtle has been its progress that few residents of the region are aware of it. It is quite invisible to the tourist who finds this wrecked landscape colorful and charming (as indeed it is, but it bears scant resemblance to what it was in 1848).

This same landscape was 'developed' once before, but with quite different results. The Pueblo Indians settled the Southwest in pre-Columbian times, but they happened *not* to be equipped with range livestock. Their civilization expired, but not because their land expired.

In India, regions devoid of any sod-forming grass have been settled, apparently without wrecking the land, by the simple expedient of carrying the grass to the cow, rather than vice versa. (Was this the result of some deep wisdom, or was it just good luck? I do not know.)

In short, the plant succession steered the course of history; the pioneer simply demonstrated, for good or ill, what successions inhered in the land. Is history taught in this spirit? It will be, once the concept of land as a community really penetrates our intellectual life.

The Ecological Conscience

Conservation is a state of harmony between men and land. Despite nearly a century of propaganda, conservation still proceeds at a snail's pace; progress still consists largely of letterhead pieties and convention oratory. On the back forty we still slip two steps backward for each forward stride.

The usual answer to this dilemma is 'more conservation education.' No one will debate this, but is it certain that only the *volume* of education needs stepping up? Is something lacking in the *content* as well?

It is difficult to give a fair summary of its content in brief form, but, as I understand it, the content is substantially this: obey the law, vote right, join some organizations, and practice what conservation is profitable on your own land; the government will do the rest.

Is not this formula too easy to accomplish anything worth-while? It defines no right or wrong, assigns no obligation, calls for no sacrifice, implies no change in the current philosophy of values. In respect of land-use, it urges only enlightened self-interest. Just how far will such education take us? An example will perhaps yield a partial answer.

By 1930 it had become clear to all except the ecologically blind that southwestern Wisconsin's topsoil was slipping seaward. In 1933 the farmers were told that if they would adopt certain remedial practices for five years, the public would donate CCC labor to install them, plus the necessary machinery and materials. The offer was widely accepted, but the practices were widely forgotten when the five-year contract period was up. The farmers continued only those practices that yielded an immediate and visible economic gain for themselves.

This led to the idea that maybe farmers would learn more quickly if they themselves wrote the rules. Accordingly the Wisconsin Legislature in 1937 passed the Soil Conservation District Law. This said to farmers, in effect: *We, the public, will furnish you free technical service and loan you specialized machinery, if you will write your own rules for land-use. Each county may write its own rules, and these will have the force of law.* Nearly all the counties promptly organized to accept the proffered help, but after a decade of operation, *no county has yet written a single rule.* There has been visible progress in such practices as strip-cropping, pasture renovation, and soil liming, but none in fencing woodlots against grazing, and none in excluding plow and cow from steep slopes. The farmers, in short, have selected those remedial practices which were profitable anyhow, and ignored those which were profitable to the community, but not clearly profitible to themselves.

When one asks why no rules have been written, one is told that the community is not yet ready to support them; education must precede rules. But the education actually in progress makes no mention of obligations to land over and above those dictated by self-interest. The net result is that we have more education but less soil, fewer healthy woods, and as many floods as in 1937.

The puzzling aspect of such situations is that the existence of obligations over and above self-interest is taken for granted in such rural community enterprises as the betterment of roads, schools, churches, and baseball teams. Their existence is not taken for granted, nor as yet seriously discussed, in bettering the behavior of the water that falls on the land, or in the preserving of the beauty or diversity of the farm landscape. Land-use ethics are still governed wholly by economic self-interest, just as social ethics were a century ago.

To sum up: we asked the farmer to do what he conveniently could to save his soil, and he has done just that, and only that. The farmer who clears the woods off a 75 percent slope, turns his cows into the clearing, and dumps its rainfall, rocks, and soil into the community creek, is still (if otherwise decent) a respected member of society. If he puts lime on his fields and plants his crops on contour, he is still entitled to all the privileges and emoluments of his Soil Conservation District. The District is a beautiful piece of social machinery, but it is coughing along on two cylinders because we have been too timid, and too anxious for quick success, to tell the farmer the true magnitude of his obligations. Obligations have no meaning without conscience, and the problem we face is the extension of the social conscience from people to land.

No important change in ethics was ever accomplished without an internal change in our intellectual emphasis, loyalties, affections, and convictions. The proof that conservation has not yet touched these foundations of conduct lies in the fact that philosophy and religion have not yet heard of it. In our attempt to make conservation easy, we have made it trivial.

Substitutes for a Land Ethic

When the logic of history hungers for bread and we hand out a stone, we are at pains to explain how much the stone resembles bread. I now describe some of the stones which serve in lieu of a land ethic.

One basic weakness in a conservation system based wholly on economic motives is that most members of the land community have no economic value. Wildflowers and songbirds are examples. Of the 22,000 higher plants and animals native to Wisconsin, it is doubtful whether more than 5 per cent can be sold, fed, eaten, or otherwise put to economic use. Yet these creatures are members of the biotic community, and if (as I believe) its stability depends on its integrity, they are entitled to continuance.

When one of these non-economic categories is threatened, and if we happen to love it, we invent subterfuges to give it economic importance. At the beginning of the century songbirds were supposed to be disappearing. Ornithologists jumped to the rescue with some distinctly shaky evidence to the effect that insects would eat us up if birds failed to control them. The evidence had to be economic in order to be valid.

It is painful to read these circumlocutions today. We have no land ethic yet, but we have at least drawn nearer the point of admitting that birds should continue as a matter of biotic right, regardless of the presence or absence of economic advantage to us.

A parallel situation exists in respect of predatory mammals, raptorial birds, and fish-eating birds. Time was when biologists somewhat overworked the evidence that these creatures preserve the health of game by killing weaklings, or that they control rodents for the farmer, or that they prey only on 'worthless' species. Here again, the evidence had to be economic in order to be valid. It is only in recent years that we hear the more honest argument that predators are members of the community, and that no special interest has the right to exterminate them for the sake of a benefit, real or fancied, to itself. Unfortunately this enlightened view is still in the talk stage. In the field the extermination of predators goes merrily on: witness the impending erasure of the timber wolf by fiat of Congress, the Conservation Bureaus, and many state legislatures.

Some species of trees have been 'read out of the party' by economics-minded foresters because they grow too slowly, or have too low a sale value to pay as timber crops: white cedar, tamarack, cypress, beech, and hemlock are examples. In Europe, where forestry is ecologically more advanced, the non-commercial tree species are recognized as members of the native forest community, to be preserved as such, within reason. Moreover some (like beech) have been found to have a valuable function in building up soil fertility. The interdependence of the forest and its constituent tree species, ground flora, and fauna is taken for granted.

Lack of economic value is sometimes a character not only of species or groups, but of entire biotic communities: marshes, bogs, dunes, and 'deserts' are examples. Our formula in such cases is to relegate their conservation to government as refuges, monuments, or parks. The difficulty is that these communities are usually interspersed with more valuable private lands; the government cannot possibly own or control such scattered parcels. The net effect is that we have relegated some of them to ultimate extinction over large areas. If the private owner were ecologically minded, he would be proud to be the custodian of a reasonable proportion of such areas, which add diversity and beauty to his farm and to his community.

In some instances, the assumed lack of profit in these 'waste' areas has proved to be wrong, but only after most of them had been done away with. The present scramble to reflood muskrat marshes is a case in point.

There is a clear tendency in American conservation to relegate to government all necessary jobs that private landowners fail to perform. Government ownership, operation, subsidy, or regulation is now widely prevalent in forestry, range management, soil and watershed management, park and wilderness conservation, fisheries management, and migratory bird management, with more to come. Most of this growth in governmental conservation is proper and logical, some of it is inevitable. That I imply no disapproval of it is implicit in the fact that I have spent most of my life working for it. Nevertheless the question arises: What is the ultimate magnitude of the enterprise? Will the tax base carry its eventual ramifications? At what point will governmental conservation, like the mastodon, become handicapped by its own dimensions? The answer, if there is any, seems to be in a land ethic, or some other force which assigns more obligation to the private landowner.

Industrial landowners and users, especially lumbermen and stockmen, are inclined to wail long and loudly about the extension of government ownership and regulation to land, but (with notable exceptions) they show little disposition to develop the only visible alternative: the voluntary practice of conservation on their own lands.

When the private landowner is asked to perform some unprofitable act for the good of the community, he today assents only with outstretched palm. If the act costs him cash this is fair and proper, but when it costs only fore-thought, open-mindedness, or time, the issue is at least debatable. The overwhelming growth of land-use subsidies in recent years must be ascribed, in large part, to the government's own agencies for conservation education: the land bureaus, the agricultural colleges, and the extension services. As far as I can detect, no ethical obligation toward land is taught in these institutions.

To sum up: a system of conservation based solely on economic self-interest is hopelessly lopsided. It tends to ignore, and thus eventually to eliminate, many elements in the land community that lack commercial value, but that are (as far as we know) essential to its healthy functioning. It assumes, falsely, I think, that the economic parts of the biotic clock will function without the uneconomic parts. It tends to relegate to government many functions eventually too large, too complex, or too widely dispersed to be performed by government.

An ethical obligation on the part of the private owner is the only visible remedy for these situations.

The Land Pyramid

An ethic to supplement and guide the economic relation to land presupposes the existence of some mental image of land as a biotic mechanism. We can be ethical only in relation to something we can see, feel, understand, love, or otherwise have faith in.

The image commonly employed in conservation education is 'the balance of nature.' For reasons too lengthy to detail here, this figure of speech fails to describe accurately what little we know about the land mechanism. A much truer image is the one employed in ecology: the biotic pyramid. I shall first sketch the pyramid as a symbol of land, and later develop some of its implications in terms of land-use.

Plants absorb energy from the sun. This energy flows through a circuit called the biota, which may be represented by a pyramid consisting of layers. The bottom layer is the soil. A plant layer rests on the soil, an insect layer on the plants, a bird and rodent layer on the insects, and so on up through various animal groups to the apex layer, which consists of the larger carnivores.

The species of a layer are alike not in where they came from, or in what they look like, but rather in what they eat. Each successive layer depends on those below it for food and often for other services, and each in turn furnishes food and services to those above. Proceeding upward, each successive layer decreases in numerical abundance. Thus, for every carnivore there are hundreds of his prey, thousands of their prey, millions of insects, uncountable plants. The pyramidal form of the system reflects this numerical progression from apex to base. Man shares an intermediate layer with the bears, raccoons, and squirrels which eat both meat and vegetables.

The lines of dependency for food and other services are called food chains. Thus soil-oak-deer-Indian is a chain that has now been largely converted to soil-corn-cow-farmer. Each species, including ourselves, is a link in many chains. The deer eats a hundred plants other than oak, and the cow a hundred plants other than corn. Both, then, are links in a hundred chains. The pyramid is a tangle of chains so complex as to seem disorderly, yet the stability of the system proves it to be a highly organized structure. Its functioning depends on the co-operation and competition of its diverse parts.

In the beginning, the pyramid of life was low and squat; the food chains short and simple. Evolution has added layer after layer, link after link. Man is one of thousands of accretions to the height and complexity of the pyramid. Science has given us many doubts, but it has given us at least one certainty: the trend of evolution is to elaborate and diversify the biota.

Land, then, is not merely soil; it is a fountain of energy flowing through a circuit of soils, plants, and animals. Food chains are the living channels which conduct energy upward; death and decay return it to the soil. The circuit is not closed; some energy is dissipated in decay, some is added by absorption from the air, some is stored in soils, peats, and long-lived forests; but it is a sustained circuit, like a slowly augmented revolving fund of life. There is always a net loss by downhill wash, but this is normally small and offset by the decay of rocks. It is deposited in the ocean and, in the course of geological time, raised to form new lands and new pyramids.

The velocity and character of the upward flow of energy depend on the complex structure of the plant and animal community, much as the upward flow of sap in a tree depends on its complex cellular organization. Without this complexity, normal circulation would presumably not occur. Structure means the characteristic numbers, as well as the characteristic kinds and functions, of the component species. This interdependence between the complex structure of the land and its smooth functioning as an energy unit is one of its basic attributes.

When a change occurs in one part of the circuit, many other parts must adjust themselves to it. Change does not necessarily obstruct or divert the flow of energy; evolution is a long series of self-induced changes, the net result of which has been to elaborate the flow mechanism and to lengthen the circuit. Evolutionary changes, however, are usually slow, and local. Man's invention of tools has enabled him to make changes of unprecedented violence, rapidity, and scope.

One change is in the composition of floras and faunas. The larger predators are lopped off the apex of the pyramid; food chains, for the first time in history, become shorter rather than longer. Domesticated species from other lands are substituted for wild ones, and wild ones are moved to new habitats. In this world-wide pooling of faunas and floras, some species get out of bounds as pests and diseases, others are extinguished. Such effects are seldom intended or foreseen; they represent unpredicted and often untraceable readjustments in the structure. Agricultural science is largely a race between the emergence of new pests and the emergence of new techniques for their control.

Another change touches the flow of energy through plants and animals and its return to the soil. Fertility is the ability of soil to receive, store, and release energy. Agriculture, by overdrafts on the soil, or by too radical a substitution of domestic for native species in the superstructure, may derange the channels of flow or deplete storage. Soils depleted of their storage, or of the organic matter which anchors it, wash away faster than they form. This is erosion.

Waters, like soil, are part of the energy circuit. Industry, by polluting waters or obstructing them with dams, may exclude the plants and animals necessary to keep energy in circulation.

Transportation brings about another basic change: the plants or animals grown in one region are now consumed and returned to the soil in another. Transportation taps the energy stored in rocks, and in the air, and uses it elsewhere; thus we fertilize the garden with nitrogen gleaned by the guano birds from the fishes of seas on the other side of the Equator. Thus the formerly localized and self-contained circuits are pooled on a world-wide scale.

The process of altering the pyramid for human occupation releases stored energy, and this often gives rise, during the pioneering period, to a deceptive exuberance of plant and animal life, both wild and tame. These releases of biotic capital tend to becloud or postpone the penalties of violence.

• • •

This thumbnail sketch of land as an energy circuit conveys three basic ideas:

(1) That land is not merely soil.

(2) That the native plants and animals kept the energy circuit open; others may or may not.

(3) That man-made changes are of a different order than evolutionary changes, and have effects more comprehensive than is intended or foreseen.

These ideas, collectively, raise two basic issues: Can the land adjust itself to the new order? Can the desired alterations be accomplished with less violence?

Biotas seem to differ in their capacity to sustain violent conversion. Western Europe, for example, carries a far different pyramid than Caesar found there. Some large animals are lost; swampy forests have become meadows or plowland; many new plants and animals are introduced, some of which escape as pests; the remaining natives are greatly changed in distribution and abundance. Yet the soil is still there and, with the help of imported nutrients, still fertile; the waters flow normally; the new structure seems to function and to persist. There is no visible stoppage or derangement of the circuit.

Western Europe, then, has a resistant biota. Its inner processes are tough, elastic, resistant to strain. No matter how violent the alterations, the pyramid, so far, has developed some new *modus vivendi* which preserves its habitability for man, and for most of the other natives.

Japan seems to present another instance of radical conversion without disorganization.

Most other civilized regions, and some as yet barely touched by civilization, display various stages of disorganization, varying from initial symptoms to advanced wastage. In Asia Minor and North Africa diagnosis is confused by climatic changes, which may have been either the cause or the effect of advanced wastage. In the United States the degree of disorganization varies locally; it is worst in the Southwest, the Ozarks, and parts of the South, and least in New England and the Northwest. Better land-uses may still arrest it in the less advanced regions. In parts of Mexico, South America, South Africa, and Australia a violent and accelerating wastage is in progress, but I cannot assess the prospects.

This almost world-wide display of disorganization in the land seems to be similar to disease in an animal, except that it never culminates in complete disorganization or death. The land recovers, but at some reduced level of complexity, and with a reduced carrying capacity for people, plants, and animals. Many biotas currently regarded as 'lands of opportunity' are in fact already subsisting on exploitative agriculture, i.e. they have already exceeded their sustained carrying capacity. Most of South America is overpopulated in this sense.

In arid regions we attempt to offset the process of wastage by reclamation, but it is only too evident that the prospective longevity of reclamation projects is often short. In our own West, the best of them may not last a century.

The combined evidence of history and ecology seems to support one general deduction: the less violent the man-made changes, the greater the probability of successful readjustment in the pyramid. Violence, in turn, varies with human population density; a dense population requires a more violent conversion. In this respect, North America has a better chance for permanence than Europe, if she can contrive to limit her density.

This deduction runs counter to our current philosophy, which assumes that because a small increase in density enriched human life, that an indefinite increase will enrich it indefinitely. Ecology knows of no density relationship that holds for indefinitely wide limits. All gains from density are subject to a law of diminishing returns.

Whatever may be the equation for men and land, it is improbable that we as yet know all its terms. Recent discoveries in mineral and vitamin nutrition reveal unsuspected dependencies in the up-circuit: incredibly minute quantities of certain substances determine the value of soils to plants, of plants to animals. What of the down-circuit? What of the vanishing species, the preservation of which we now regard as an esthetic luxury? They helped build the soil; in what unsuspected ways may they be essential to its maintenance? Professor Weaver proposes that we use prairie flowers to reflocculate the wasting soils of the dust bowl; who knows for what purpose cranes, and condors, otters and grizzlies may some day be used?

Land Health and the A-B Cleavage

A land ethic, then, reflects the existence of an ecological conscience, and this in turn reflects a conviction of individual responsibility for the health of the land. Health is the capacity of the land for self-renewal. Conservation is our effort to understand and preserve this capacity.

Conservationists are notorious for their dissensions. Superficially these seem to add up to mere confusion, but a more careful scrutiny reveals a single plane of cleavage common to many specialized fields. In each field one group (A) regards the land as soil, and its function as commodity-production; another group (B) regards the land as a biota, and its function as something broader. How much broader is admittedly in a state of doubt and confusion.

In my own field, forestry, group A is quite content to grow trees like cabbages, with cellulose as the basic forest commodity. It feels no inhibition against violence; its ideology is agronomic. Group B, on the other hand, sees forestry as fundamentally different from agronomy because it employs natural species, and manages a natural environment rather than creating an artificial one. Group B prefers natural reproduction on principle. It worries on biotic as well as economic grounds about the loss of species like chestnut, and the threatened loss of the white pines. It worries about a whole series of secondary forest functions: wildlife, recreation, watersheds, wilderness areas. To my mind, Group B feels the stirrings of an ecological conscience.

In the wildlife field, a parallel cleavage exists. For Group A the basic commodities are sport and meat; the yardsticks of production are ciphers of take in pheasants and trout. Artificial propagation is acceptable as a permanent as well as a temporary recourse—if its unit costs permit. Group B, on the other hand, worries about a whole series of biotic side-issues. What is the cost in predators of producing a game crop? Should we have further recourse to exotics? How can management restore the shrinking species, like prairie grouse, already hopeless as shootable game? How can management restore the threatened ratites, like trumpeter swan and whooping crane? Can management principles be extended to wildflowers? Here again it is clear to me that we have the same A-B cleavage as in forestry.

In the larger field of agriculture I am less competent to speak, but there seem to be somewhat parallel cleavages. Scientific agriculture was actively developing before ecology was born, hence a slower penetration of ecological concepts might be expected. Moreover the farmer, by the very nature of his techniques, must modify the biota more radically than the forester or the wildlife manager. Nevertheless, there are many discontents in agriculture which seem to add up to a new vision of 'biotic farming.'

Perhaps the most important of these is the new evidence that poundage or tonnage is no measure of the food-value of farm crops; the products of fertile soil may be qualitatively as well as quantitatively superior. We can bolster poundage from depleted soils by pouring on imported fertility, but we are not necessarily bolstering food-value. The possible ultimate ramifications of this idea are so immense that I must leave their exposition to abler pens.

The discontent that labels itself 'organic farming,' while bearing some of the earmarks of a cult, is nevertheless biotic in its direction, particularly in its insistence on the importance of soil flora and fauna.

The ecological fundamentals of agriculture are just as poorly known to the public as in other fields of land-use. For example, few educated people realize that the marvelous advances in technique made during recent decades are improvements in the pump, rather than the well. Acre for acre, they have barely sufficed to offset the sinking level of fertility.

In all of these cleavages, we see repeated the same basic paradoxes: man the conqueror *versus* man the biotic citizen; science the sharpener of his sword *versus* science the searchlight on his universe; land the slave and servant *versus* land the collective organism. Robinson's injunction to Tristram may well be applied, at this juncture, to *Homo sapiens* as a species in geological time:

> Whether you will or not
> You are a King, Tristram, for you are one
> Of the time-tested few that leave the world,
> When they are gone, not the same place it was.
> Mark what you leave.

The Outlook

It is inconceivable to me that an ethical relation to land can exist without love, respect, and admiration for land, and a high regard for its value. By value, I of course mean something far broader than mere economic value; I mean value in the philosophical sense.

Perhaps the most serious obstacle impeding the evolution of a land ethic is the fact that our educational and economic system is headed away from, rather than toward, an intense consciousness of land. Your true modern is separated from the land by many middlemen, and by innumerable physical gadgets. He has no vital relation to it; to him it is the space between cities on which crops grow. Turn him loose for a day on the land, and if the spot does not happen to be a golf links or a 'scenic' area, he is bored stiff. If crops could be raised by hydroponics instead of farming, it would suit him very well. Synthetic substitutes for wood, leather, wool, and other natural land products suit him better than the originals. In short, land is something he has 'outgrown.'

Almost equally serious as an obstacle to a land ethic is the attitude of the farmer for whom the land is still an adversary, or a taskmaster that keeps him in slavery. Theoretically, the mechanization of farming ought to cut the farmer's chains, but whether it really does is debatable.

One of the requisites for an ecological comprehension of land is an understanding of ecology, and this is by no means co-extensive with 'education'; in fact, much higher education seems deliberately to avoid ecological concepts. An understanding of ecology does not necessarily originate in courses bearing ecological labels; it is quite as likely to be labeled geography, botany, agronomy, history, or economics. This is as it should be, but whatever the label, ecological training is scarce.

The case for a land ethic would appear hopeless but for the minority which is in obvious revolt against these 'modern' trends.

The 'key-log' which must be moved to release the evolutionary process for an ethic is simply this: quit thinking about decent land-use as solely an economic problem. Examine each question in terms of what is ethically and esthetically right, as well as what is economically expedient. A thing is right when it tends to preserve the integrity, stability, and beauty of the biotic community. It is wrong when it tends otherwise.

It of course goes without saying that economic feasibility limits the tether of what can or cannot be done for land. It always has and it always will. The fallacy the economic determinists have tied around our collective neck, and which we now need to cast off, is the belief that economics determines *all* land-use. This is simply not true. An innumerable host of actions and attitudes, comprising perhaps the bulk of all land relations, is determined by the land-users' tastes and predilections, rather than by his purse. The bulk of all land relations hinges on investments of time, forethought, skill, and faith rather than on investments of cash. As a land-user thinketh, so is he.

I have purposely presented the land ethic as a product of social evolution because nothing so important as an ethic is ever 'written.' Only the most superficial student of history supposes that Moses 'wrote' the Decalogue; it evolved in the minds of a thinking community, and Moses wrote a tentative summary of it for a 'seminar.' I say tentative because evolution never stops.

The evolution of a land ethic is an intellectual as well as emotional process. Conservation is paved with good intentions which prove to be futile, or even dangerous, because they are devoid of critical understanding either of the land, or of economic land-use. I think it is a truism that as the ethical frontier advances from the individual to the community, its intellectual content increases.

The mechanism of operation is the same for any ethic: social approbation for right actions: social disapproval for wrong actions.

By and large, our present problem is one of attitudes and implements. We are remodeling the Alhambra with a steam-shovel, and we are proud of our yardage. We shall hardly relinquish the shovel, which after all has many good points, but we are in need of gentler and more objective criteria for its successful use.

Excerpt from *The Swamp: The Everglades, Florida, and the Politics of Paradise*

Endgame

Michael Grunwald

> We view this as the most important year in our history.
> —Everglades Coalition, January 2000 agenda

A Time to Act

The slogan for the January 2000 Everglades Coalition conference in Naples was "A Time to Act." The political climate may not have been ideal, but momentum had been building for eight years, and the coalition's leaders were convinced that 2000 would be their best chance—perhaps their last chance—to pass a restoration project. It was also the decision year for the Homestead airport, the most prominent threat to the ecosystem in a generation. "Action taken to restore the Everglades in the next year will set the course for the next several decades," the agenda said.

Over the course of the twentieth century, Florida conservationists had helped stop plume hunts, preserve millions of acres of wetlands, mandate minimum flows to Everglades National Park, and secure the largest nutrient cleanup in history. But the Everglades was still dying. The ecosystem's natural balance was so out of whack that efforts to save the Cape Sable sparrow threatened the survival of the Everglade snail kite. Cattails were still spreading, tree islands were vanishing, muck soils were shrinking, estuaries were collapsing, and development was blocking the recharge of the region's groundwater. The greatest enemy of the Everglades, the coalition's leaders declared, was further delay.

• • •

Senator Chafee had promised to hold a field hearing on the Comprehensive Everglades Restoration Plan at the Naples conference, and Senator Smith agreed to respect his late predecessor's wishes. Everglades activists were not expecting much from the John Birch Society's top-rated senator; after he took over the committee, the Sierra Club attacked him as "a fox in charge of the henhouse," and one journalist wrote that "many environmental groups are predicting an apocalypse of sorts." They never dreamed he would be one of the Everglades plan's most aggressive champions.

"John Chafee was strongly committed to seeing this restoration effort go forward," Smith said in his opening statement. "I totally agree. You will find no daylight between Senator Chafee's position and my own." The crowd gasped, and then cheered. Smith was a devout Roman Catholic, and he believed in the sanctity of life—not only for unborn children, but for egrets and otters, too. His six-year-old son had seen his first alligator on a vacation in the Everglades, and Smith now saw the swamp as a test for mankind: "When our distant descendants move into the Fourth Millennium, I hope it will be remembered that this generation, at the beginning of the Third Millennium, put aside partisanship, narrow self-interest and short-term thinking by saving the Everglades." Smith was as conservative as it got in American politics, but he figured that part of conservatism meant conserving things.

Senator Smith's witnesses were divided over the details of CERP, especially the Chief's Report's elevation of nature over people. But every key witness supported the Restudy. U.S. Sugar's Bubba Wade distanced the sugar industry from Citizens for a Sound Economy, and said growers now welcomed the restoration plan. Nathaniel Reed, the Everglades Coalition's elder statesman, answered the question of whether the plan would work with "an unequivocal yes!" Even Dexter Lehtinen, who devoted most of his testimony to Miccosukee grievances against the Interior Department, praised the Army Corps technical plan. Governor Bush's environmental secretary, David Struhs, quoted Senator Holland's remarks after the passage of the original C&SF Project: "The whole Florida delegation has stuck together in this matter and will, I am sure, continue to do so. The Florida citizens, industries and public units have also cooperated to the fullest degree, as has the Republican delegation. I want you to remember that this is not a partisan project, and should continue to merit the united efforts of all our people."

"That quote is as applicable in 2000 as it was in 1948," Struhs said.

The Everglades Coalition couldn't have scripted a much better start for its push for action. The restoration plan suddenly seemed sacrosanct; Senator Inhofe was the only politician who publicly opposed it, and he had no power over it. Even Senator Voinovich declared that he supported it despite his concerns about its cost and uncertainty; to be safe, Smith decided to yank the plan out of Voinovich's subcommittee and oversee it himself. "Both parties are sticking to the we-love-the-Everglades script," the *Palm Beach Post* said. Clinton administration officials met with Bush's aides in Naples, and were pleasantly surprised to hear that the governor felt as strongly as they did about swift action. Allison DeFoor, Bush's Everglades czar, called 2000 a "do-or-die year," and vowed that Florida would fund its share of CERP by the end of the spring.

DeFoor sensed that south Florida's interest groups were like drunks at the end of a bar fight. Their arms felt heavy, and they wanted an excuse to stop slugging. DeFoor set up a meeting between Audubon activists and sugar growers at Paul Tudor Jones's estate on the Keys, and both sides agreed over stone crabs to support the governor's funding bill. But the good feelings went only so far; a U.S. Sugar executive could not resist stealing one of Jones's prize orchids before he left.

Before the Naples conference ended, Secretary Babbitt—back in good graces with his old antagonists in the Everglades Coalition—provided a final jolt of welcome news, announcing his personal opposition to the Homestead airport. A recent draft of the Clinton administration's revised study had suggested that the airport was back on track, but EPA Administrator Browner now came out against it as well. The administration was clearly divided, which meant the decision would be made in the White House.

Alan Farago, the Sierra Club activist leading the airport opposition, always figured the fight would come down to raw politics. Dade County's backroom deals reminded him of the corruption in his hometown of Providence, with Cubans instead of Italians calling the shots. But Farago believed the influence-peddlers could be defeated—not by playing kissy-face with decision-makers, but by building so much public revulsion to the airport that decision-makers would be afraid to approve it. He had quit an Audubon board out of disgust with the group's insider compromises, and he wanted to show that principled grass-roots activism could produce results.

Farago faced an uphill battle. Dade County Mayor Alex Penelas, the most prominent Cuban-American Democrat, was the airport's leading supporter. And Jorge Mas Santos, the leader of the Cuban American National Foundation—the anti-Castro group that dominated Miami exile politics—was one of the airport's key investors. President Clinton had won Florida in 1996 by making new inroads among Cuban voters and donors, and Vice President Gore's advisers feared that alienating Penelas, Mas, and the Latin Builders Association—not to mention Senator Graham—would doom his chances in Florida in 2000. Gore was already scrambling to distance himself from the Clinton administration's handling of Elián González, the five-year-old shipwreck survivor who had become a figure of religious devotion in Little Havana. Some Cuban-American leaders felt just as strongly about the Homestead issue; in fact, rumors were flying that they had offered the boy to the administration in exchange for a guarantee of the airport.

The airport's opponents also faced a serious cash disadvantage. The developers were paying more than $1 million to one of Washington's top lobbying firms, Verner, Liipfert, whose partners included former Senate Majority Leaders Bob Dole and George Mitchell. They also bankrolled an "Equal Justice Coalition," which spread the word that airport opponents were racists who wanted to keep minorities in poverty. The Sierra Club could barely afford buttons and T-shirts. But Farago noticed that Dade County's flight plans for the new airport passed directly over the Ocean Reef Club, a north Key Largo enclave of two thousand of America's wealthiest snowbirds. On his first visit, he met an elderly investor named Lloyd Schumaker, who wrote him a $100,000 check before he could even finish explaining why he was there. When Farago explained that the donation would not be tax-deductible, the crotchety Schumaker said he didn't care; he had already made $30 million that year.

Ocean Reef's residents ultimately decided to tax themselves to provide Farago with a $2 million war chest. That was enough to launch a sophisticated campaign, with pollsters, lobbyists, economic consultants, a Cuban-American community organizer, and slick ads depicting a flock of jets flying over Biscayne Bay, under the caption: Somehow, It's Not Quite the Same. The basic message was that it made no sense for the federal government to green-light a major airport at the edge of the Everglades at the same time it wanted taxpayers to spend $8 billion to restore the Everglades.

The campaign soon converted Senator Voinovich to its cause, partly because Ocean Reef was home to a number of well-connected Ohio Republicans, partly because the senator wanted to prove he cared about the Everglades despite his skepticism about the restoration plan. The usually mild-mannered Senator Mack once yelled at him to mind his own business, but Voinovich believed that if the Everglades was really "America's Everglades," as the Florida senators kept calling it, then a threat to the Everglades was America's business.

The main target of the campaign was Al Gore, who had the power to kill or approve the airport. But the vice president refused to take a stand—even after Babbitt and Browner sided with environmentalists, even after former senator Bill Bradley, his challenger for the Democratic presidential nomination, came out against the airport as well. Gore would only pledge to seek "a balanced solution" that would help the economy without harming the environment. As a public servant, Gore was often far ahead of his colleagues on issues like nuclear proliferation, environmental protection, and the "information superhighway," but as a politician, he had a tendency to straddle.

Gore's aides assumed that Florida activists would forgive him for taking a pass; after all, he had demanded the additional study that held up the airport in 1997, and had spearheaded the plan to restore the Everglades. But the airport's opponents kept up the pressure. In February, they threatened to protest an "Environmental Voters for Gore" rally in Broward County, scheduled to feature Browner with actors Leonardo DiCaprio and Ted Danson. The Gore campaign was afraid of man-bites-dog articles about conservationists attacking the Ozone Man, so the rally was cancelled. "Al Gore spilled blood for these people for eight years, and they were going to protest?" recalled Mitchell Berger, a Fort Lauderdale attorney and Democratic fund-raiser who was Gore's closest confidant in Florida. "Talk about the death of common sense."

Politically, Gore was walking a fine line between Democratic-leaning environmentalists and Republican-leaning Cuban-Americans. But the airport's opponents assumed he would return to his green roots after the predawn raid of April 22, when armed federal agents seized Elián from his Miami relatives so that his father could take him back to Cuba. There was no way Gore could distance himself from the administration now; Nathaniel Reed told the vice president's aides he wouldn't win the Cuban vote if he promised to land the 82nd Airborne in Havana. And it was hard to imagine that Gore still cared about Mayor Penelas, who had made national headlines by declaring that the administration would be responsible if Miami rioted over Elián.

Yet Gore remained on the fence. He wasn't convinced that the airport was central to the plumbing problems that were destroying the Everglades. Neither one of his most trusted Everglades advisers, Berger and Paul Tudor Jones, had raised alarms about the airport; in fact, Berger did legal work for the Mas family, and had once told environmentalists that he could engineer a buyout of the Eight-and-a-Half Square Mile Area if they would back off the airport. Berger helped persuade Gore that the airport opposition had more to do with not-in-my-backyard complaints about noise over Ocean Reef—a vacation getaway for prominent Republicans such as Senate Appropriations Chairman Ted Stevens of Alaska—than ecological concern for the River of Grass. "I didn't think the airport threatened the survival of the Everglades," Gore later recalled. In any case, Gore's advisers figured Everglades activists would back him regardless of Homestead. Shouldn't an $8 billion restoration plan count for something?

"Consensus Was the Only Way to Do This"

But many everglades activists remained skeptical of the restoration plan. They had grudgingly agreed to support it after the Chief's Report provided the additional commitments that it would actually restore the Everglades. But it soon became clear that the additional commitments in the Chief's Report were dead on arrival on Capitol Hill. Senators Mack and Graham—as well as Vice President Gore and Governor Bush—believed that passing CERP depended on maintaining a consensus among Florida's interest groups, and there was a consensus among every group except environmentalists that the Clinton administration had unfairly elevated nature over people. "They wrote us a letter," an aide to Mack assured Dexter Lehtinen. "We'll write them back a law."

The nonenvironmental interests all argued that the Chief's Report—especially its guarantee of 79 billion extra gallons for the park—had violated the consensus process that produced the original technical plan. Even Audubon's Tom Adams, the most active Everglades Coalition lobbyist, was sympathetic to the accusations of an end-run. Senators Mack and Graham wrote a letter protesting the guarantee, and the Clinton administration quickly backed off, saying the Corps was only committed to studying whether to provide the extra water. In the spring, Senate staffers agreed that their bill would ignore the Chief's Report, authorizing only the original Army Corps technical plan—the same technical plan that had been lambasted by the scientists at Everglades National Park. After months of cheerleading for CERP, the Everglades Coalition once again had to decide what to do about an Everglades restoration plan with questionable benefits for the Everglades.

The activists who had persuaded the Democratic administration to add environmental commitments to the Chief's Report hoped they could now persuade the Republican-controlled Senate to add environmental assurances to the actual bill, especially legal requirements that would reserve water for the Everglades and ensure ecological progress within a decade. They also wanted to maximize the power of the Department of the Interior, which tended to side with the environment, and minimize the power of the governor of Florida, who tended to side with his constituents. Unfortunately for the environmentalists, every other key stakeholder wanted the opposite. Sugar growers, home builders, water utilities, and Florida's other economic interests were all determined to make sure CERP did not favor nature over people— by eliminating or weakening environmental assurances, minimizing the power of Interior, and maximizing the power of the state. They had such a common vision for CERP that they shared the same Washington lobbyist, Robert Dawson, a courtly Alabama native who had overseen the Corps during the Reagan administration. Dawson did not mind if CERP was marketed as a pure Everglades restoration plan, but he warned that it would never get out of the bog without solid guarantees for water supply and flood control.

The Seminole and Miccosukee tribes agreed with Dawson's clients that CERP should not favor nature over Floridians. They may have considered the Everglades their mother, but they were Floridians, too, with their own economic interests; the Seminoles ran a $500-million-a-year gaming business as well as cattle and citrus operations, and the Miccosukees had just opened their own casino overlooking the Everglades. The Miccosukees were especially determined to limit the role of Interior, an institution they despised. They still considered Everglades National Park their rightful homeland, and tensions had flared again recently when park leaders tried to stop them from building homes along the Tamiami Trail. Dexter Lehtinen warned that if CERP gave Interior any power over water management in Florida, "we will put a knife in the heart of this bill."

Governor Bush also sided with the economic interests. Florida's legislature had agreed to pay half of CERP's cost without a single dissenting vote, and Bush was determined to make sure equal money meant equal power. That meant an equal balance between the Everglades and his constituents, and an equal partnership between the Corps and the state; anything less, he told Congress, would be a "master-servant relationship." Senators Graham and Mack, who were in charge of refining CERP to ensure a consensus among Florida's interest groups, tended to agree. With green groups on one side and just about everyone else on the other side, it would be easier to forge consensus by pressuring the green groups to make concessions than by pressuring everyone else.

Even within the Clinton administration, there was only limited support for trying to strengthen the bill's environmental assurances. Vice President Gore had no desire to dive into details; Mitchell Berger had told him the environmental critics were extremists who would only be satisfied if the city of Weston was reflooded. Army Corps officials generally sided with Bush and the Florida interests; they didn't want to share power with Interior, and they didn't want their hands tied by restoration requirements. And George Frampton, the former Interior official who now coordinated policy at the Clinton White House, was tired of the Everglades Coalition's whining. He just wanted to pass a bill. The only administration official willing to fight was Secretary Babbitt, who didn't care too much about the details of the plumbing, but did care about Interior's role. In March, when Frampton was about to agree to strip Interior's power over CERP, Babbitt faxed a heated letter to his former aide threatening to oppose the administration's pet project if the Corps and the state retained full control: "Otherwise we allow a future that repeats past mistakes, with grievous consequences for our children and grandchildren." Frampton backed down, and the internal split never became public.

It was the threat of a public showdown that gave Babbitt his leverage within the administration; Vice President Gore did not want to be blamed for delaying the revival of the Everglades before the election. But the Everglades Coalition did not have much leverage in the Senate to demand benefits for the environment. The coalition had secured the commitments in the Chief's Report by threatening to oppose CERP, but those threats were a lot less credible now that it had declared 2000 "A Time to Act," and national conservation organizations were clamoring for Congress to pass the bill. Environmentalists who still hoped to improve the bill could see that their chances were shrinking by the day, as Audubon and other groups began jockeying to portray themselves to funders as the saviors of the Everglades. There was intense pressure to stay "on message," to stop quibbling over details, to avoid discrediting CERP. Audubon issued one statement declaring that "we will continue to seek improvements in the bill to increase restoration benefits—as long as they do not endanger its enactment."

"Our feeling was: This isn't perfect, but it's more good than bad," said Audubon president John Flicker. Even CERP's water-supply components would reduce pressure on the Everglades, and several uncontroversial restoration components would benefit Big Cypress, the St. Lucie estuary, and Biscayne Bay's coastal wetlands. The Wall Street wizard Paul Tudor Jones told Audubon leaders that he had spent $5 million on the Everglades; he would consider $8 billion an excellent return. Larry Kast, a brash young water resources lobbyist who joined the Audubon team during CERP, advised environmentalists to stop trying to sweeten the deal. "I was focused like a laser beam on getting this passed, and the key was unity in Florida," Kast recalled. "We had to stop arguing over every frigging detail and every frigging drop of water. We had to get our shit together, or we were going to lose $8 billion."

More skeptical activists such as Environmental Defense's Tim Searchinger and NRDC's Brad Sewell knew that some of their colleagues believed they were threatening a fragile consensus, turning up their noses at an $8 billion restoration plan because it wasn't perfect. But this was the same plan the park's scientists had said "does not represent a restoration scenario for the southern, central and northern Everglades." The latest version of CERP did not even guarantee that the project would do no harm to the Everglades—only that no one's level of water supply or flood control would be reduced. That seemed a lot worse than imperfect.

On May 11, Chairman Smith and Senator Max Baucus of Montana, the ranking Democrat on Smith's committee, held the first hearing on the Everglades bill. It was supposed to be a typical congressional Kabuki show, an opportunity for flowery speeches about the majesty of the River of Grass, with Smith demonstrating the Republican commitment to restoration and Baucus carrying water for the Clinton plan. But as Baucus listened to testimony about the plan's "tremendous amount of flexibility"—and watched witnesses duck questions about its ecological uncertainties—he did something exceedingly rare in Washington. He ditched his script and spoke his mind:

> I'm a little uneasy and I'll tell you why. I worry about seeing the evening news a year or two or three from now, "The Fleecing of America," "It's Your Money," something like that. . . . I have a funny feeling that I might be buying something that sounds good, but down the road, it's going to leave my successors a huge, huge program. And the problem is, we've spent all this money on the Everglades and my gosh, it's not working like it was supposed to

work. Oh, we've gone this far, gee, it's like the Vietnam War in a
sense, we've got to keep pouring more money into it because it's
gone this far. What's our exit strategy?

An aide to the senator kept passing him notes and kicking his chair, but
Baucus kept rambling. "Nobody has provided a compelling case that
this is going to work," he blurted. "So far, it doesn't totally pass the
smell test, if you want the honest truth."

This unplanned outburst of candor offered unexpected ammunition
to Searchinger, Sewell, and other environmental critics of the restoration
bill. They contended that without strict legal assurances for the natural
system, Florida officials would keep giving away water needed for the
Everglades to cities and farms, and CERP would never pass the smell
test needed to secure national support. Governor Bush's lobbyists
argued that assurances were unnecessary; because Florida already had
the power to reserve water for the environment. But the state had only
used that power once in twenty-eight years, for a marsh in the St. Johns
basin. Senate staffers were wary of fixes that would antagonize every
lobby except the enviros, but most of them—especially Senator Smith's
aides—eventually realized the critics had a point. CERP had to change
the status quo that had destroyed the Everglades.

The problem was finding the right language that could nail down the
support of queasy environmentalists and avoid "Fleecing of America"
exposés without losing the support of the other interest groups. After
months of roller-coaster negotiations, Florida's economic interests
withdrew their support for the bill in early August, then changed their
minds after extracting a few key concessions. In early September,
Senators Graham and Mack orchestrated a settlement of every key
group, only to see Governor Bush's aides pull out of the agreement.
This time, Senator Mack called Bush and explained that the state of
Florida was holding up an excellent compromise. The governor, who
was campaigning for his brother out west, called his underlings and
told them to back down. George W. Bush didn't want to be blamed for
scuttling Everglades restoration, either.

Anyway, Jeb Bush had gotten most of what he wanted in the bill. The state would be an equal partner with the Corps, which was already sympathetic to Florida's economic interests. Interior would only have a veto over the rules governing the project, not the sixty-eight project components. Those rules would not define the natural system's water needs, as environmentalists had hoped; they would only set up "a process" to define those needs. (Bush's aides had tried to dilute the rules even further, proposing that they set up "a process to provide procedural guidance" to define those needs.) Senator Voinovich secured a resolution declaring that reuse of the Homestead air base should be compatible with Everglades restoration, but Graham and Mack fought off substantive measures that could have blocked the proposed airport. Nobody's ox would be gored by CERP.

In general, the assurances did not assure much for the Everglades, although they did impose a few restraints on state water managers. The bill stated that "the overarching purpose" of the bill was restoration, but its substantive provisions included much stronger protections for flood control and water supply. And while Senator Smith's aides did jam some extra assurances language into their committee report, highlighting the Army Corps pledge that 80 percent of the water captured by CERP would go to the environment, the report did not have the force of law.

A few environmental groups denounced the consensus legislation, most notably Friends of the Everglades, the grass-roots organization founded by Marjory Stoneman Douglas. Robert Johnson, the head of Everglades National Park's science staff, told the *Washington Post* that the legislation would do almost nothing for the environment: "This is just a situation where the emperor has no clothes." When Audubon, the National Parks Conservation Association, the National Wildlife Federation, and Defenders of Wildlife passed around a draft letter describing CERP as a "must-pass" bill, the ecologist Stuart Pimm wrote a blistering critique:

> Of course, we should all live long and healthy lives; we will need
> to do so if we are to see this plan's benefits. . . . I can see why the

sugar growers like this plan. This is a plan for ecological inaction
and that is exactly why I find fault with it. I believe that consensus
is fine. I applaud your efforts to work out compromise. But at
some level this must fail: just because the policymakers all agree
that the sun rises in the west doesn't make it so.

But most green groups went along with the deal—some with
trepidation, some with enthusiasm. "This is an historic agreement for
the future of America's Everglades," rejoiced Audubon's Stuart Strahl.
Johnson's bosses at Interior also endorsed the bill, along with the rest
of the Clinton administration. Secretary Babbitt would have preferred
solid guarantees for the natural system, but he figured all the hype over
"America's Everglades" would at least create expectations of restoration
in the future. Perhaps the sugar industry would agree to sacrifice more
land for restoration after it exhausted its soils, or after it lost its federal
price protections, or after Castro died. Perhaps prolonged water
shortages—and the rate hikes that could accompany them—would
persuade Floridians to start conserving their most precious resource.
Or maybe desalinization or some other new technology would solve
south Florida's water problems. CERP would just be a start.

The Everglades Is Coming

The plan was now in place, but Congress still had to approve it before
adjourning for the election. Army Corps bills tend to pass at the last
minute without debate, because Congress prefers to keep its pork
platters off C-SPAN. But this one still had to make it through the Senate
and House. "The single greatest threat to restoration of America's
Everglades is the lack of time left in the congressional session," said
Audubon's Strahl.

Behind the scenes, Florida's state officials, economic interests, and
tribes had all fought to reduce CERP's emphasis on nature, but they
now came together to promote it as a restoration plan for America's
Everglades. Audubon lobbyist Tom Adams walked the halls of Congress
arm-in-arm with sugar lobbyist Bob Dawson. "If we can agree to support

the Everglades," they told members, "then you should, too." Senators Smith and Mack rallied support among Republicans, while Senator Graham and the Clinton administration lined up Democrats. It wasn't too hard. When Senator Inhofe tried to persuade colleagues that CERP was an astronomically expensive, scandalously uncertain exercise in government bloat, they often replied: But it's the Everglades! Senate Majority Leader Trent Lott had no great interest in the Everglades—he joked that he was pretty sure it wasn't in Mississippi—but he fast-tracked the Corps bill as a favor to Mack.

One potential sticking point was a raging debate over "Corps reform." After a Corps economist blew the whistle on the agency's frantic efforts to justify a billion-dollar lock project on the Mississippi River, Corps follies became front-page fodder, and Corps critics called for independent reviews of major projects, setting the stage for an ugly floor fight. But the environmental establishment never pressed too hard for the reforms, because it did not want to endanger Everglades restoration. So the Corps bill went to the Senate floor without them.

Instead, the Senate debate over the bill was dominated by florid tributes to the Everglades, and to the bipartisan consensus that had brought together Florida's Hatfields and McCoys. Senator Smith read a list of endorsers ranging from the Florida Fertilizer and Agrichemical Association to the National Parks Conservation Association. Senator Graham marveled at how much had changed since he launched his Save Our Everglades program to turn back time in south Florida. "In 1983, restoring the natural health and function of this precious system seemed to be a distant dream," he said. "After seventeen years of bipartisan progress, we now stand on the brink of this dream becoming a reality." But Senators Inhofe and Voinovich were not the only voices of caution. Senator John Warner, a Republican from Virginia, complained that the Everglades would dwarf all other water projects, including the restoration of Chesapeake Bay. "All of a sudden, we come along with the romance of the Everglades," Warner said. "Paul Revere called out: The

British are coming. I call out: Folks, this is coming. You better go back home and talk to your constituents and say this one is going to be in competition with what I had planned for our state." Senator Baucus tried to defend the bill, but he again betrayed his doubts, acknowledging that part of him agreed with the critics. "This arrangement may not be perfect," Baucus said. "But we are dealing with an extraordinary, special situation, and that is the Everglades. . . . There is a slight tilt in favor of the State of Florida, but the Everglades is really special. It is a national treasure."

The Senate passed the bill by an 85 to 1 margin, with Inhofe the only dissenter. "If you have any doubts about every single 'i' being dotted and every 't' being crossed, take the risk. You'll be glad you did," Smith said. "When the historians look back, they are going to say when it came time to stand up for the Everglades, we did."

Now the house of Representatives controlled the fate of the Everglades. Momentous issues were at stake—the most ambitious ecosystem restoration in history, a new model for dealing with water conflicts, a new direction for the Corps, a chance to prove that man could repair his relationship with Mother Nature. But in the House, only one issue mattered: Clay Shaw was in a tight race. The workmanlike ten-term congressman from Fort Lauderdale was one of the most vulnerable Republicans, and with control of the House hanging on a few contested races, Speaker Dennis Hastert of Illinois was willing to do anything necessary to help the chairman of the Florida delegation. "We knew this could come down to two seats, and if that meant we had to spend $8 billion for Mr. Shaw, that's what we were going to do," one Hastert aide recalled.

In September, Shaw introduced the Senate's Everglades deal in the House, and Chairman Shuster attached it to an Army Corps bill that was so crammed with local water projects it took up forty-five pages of the *Congressional Record*. The bill had been held up all summer in a partisan dispute over prevailing-wage laws, but Republicans now agreed to drop their objections to get the Altoonaglades passed. On October 19, Shaw presided over the debate from the speaker's chair, watched a series of Republicans give him credit for saving the Everglades, and made the final speech before the House approved the bill by a 394 to 14 margin. "We are seeing a rare moment in the closing days of this Congress: both great political parties coming together and doing the right thing," Shaw crowed.

The congressional debate over the Everglades was dominated by high-minded rhetoric about the River of Grass being above partisan politics. But it was still election season, and Florida was shaping up as the key battleground between Vice President Gore and George W. Bush. The day before the House voted on CERP, Gore's campaign aides huddled with Everglades activists in Miami, pleading with them to rally their troops behind the vice president. Kathleen McGinty, Gore's top environmental adviser, began the meeting by pointing out that Gore had led the fight to restore the Everglades, taken on the sugar industry over penny-a-pound, and fought for the environment all his life. But all the activists wanted to talk about was his waffling on the Homestead airport.

The Gore campaign had never imagined that they would have to beg Florida environmentalists for support three weeks before Election Day. George W. Bush was the dream candidate of drilling, mining, and logging interests; Gore was their nightmare. When a Democratic operative had tried to warn Gore campaign manager Donna Brazile that Everglades activists were irate about Homestead, the message had come back: "Tell them to go fuck themselves." Where else could environmentalists turn?

The answer, for some of them, had been Ralph Nader, the consumer crusader who was running on the Green Party ticket, attacking Bush and Gore as twin peas in a corporate pod. Joe Browder, a lifelong Democrat, had begun feeding information on Homestead to the Nader campaign and a group called Environmentalists Against Gore, and Nader had started making speeches denouncing the airport plan and accusing Gore of selling out the Everglades. Alan Farago had refused to take Nader's calls, but he knew the airport was costing Gore votes. In September, he had commissioned a Democratic pollster to conduct a survey of Florida voters, which suggested that Gore would gain four points if he came out against the airport. The Sierra Club had given the results to Gore's campaign, but the vice president refused to switch his position.

Even Nathaniel Reed, the ultimate inside player, had grown exasperated after months of behind-the-scenes lobbying against the airport. The vice president's aides had promised Reed that he would make an anti-airport speech, and Reed tended to err on the side of trust, especially with eco-friendly politicians like the Ozone Man. But he eventually realized that Gore had no intention of getting off the fence, and he fired off an e-mail throughout the environmental community, warning that Gore was contemplating the destruction of two beloved parks. "Until the Administration and in particular the Vice President is confronted with opposition, the Administration will continue to ignore the issue," Reed wrote. "From crisis comes opportunity! Force the crisis!"

Now it was three weeks before the election, and the Gore campaign realized it had a Nader crisis in south Florida. McGinty, Gore confidant Mitchell Berger, and former water management district director Sam Poole were dispatched to try to persuade the enviros that Homestead was a crazy litmus test. McGinty argued that Gore had gone to bat for the environment for his entire career; it was time for environmentalists to go to bat for Gore. But the activists just wanted to know why he had stayed in the on-deck circle on the airport. They said his silence was driving their members to Nader.

Berger couldn't believe he was having this conversation. George W. Bush hadn't taken a position on the airport. Neither had Jeb Bush. And Gore at least had an excuse for staying mum; the administration's study was still under way, and taking sides could be construed as interference. Anyway, Gore had intervened to block the initial pro-airport study; didn't that suggest his true feelings? Babbitt and Browner publicly opposed the airport; didn't that suggest where the decision was headed? If Gore made a statement now, it would just look like pandering. "Isn't there any trust in this room?" Berger asked.

There wasn't much. One airport opponent challenged Berger on his work for Jorge Mas; Berger insisted it didn't matter. McGinty said Gore wanted to hold an environmental rally in south Florida to highlight his defense of the Everglades, and asked whether there would be protesters. Absolutely, she was told. "Tell him that only a true friend will tell you what you don't want to hear," one activist said. "And what you don't want to hear is that you are going to lose this election because of Homestead."

Meanwhile, the Everglades plan was in danger yet again. The House and Senate had to reconcile their Army Corps bills, and Senator Smith objected to a half-billion dollars of "environmental infrastructure" in the House bill. He knew "environmental infrastructure" was a euphemism for water and sewer plants, which were supposed to be local responsibilities. The Corps was already under fire for General Ballard's "Program Growth Initiative," and Smith didn't want to encourage more mission creep. He told Chairman Shuster he would block the bill unless the extra pork was removed.

Shuster was flabbergasted. A committee chairman objecting to the presence of pork in a Corps bill was like a Burger King fry cook objecting to the presence of beef in a Whopper. Environmental infrastructure was especially dear to Shuster's heart; he had invented the concept in a 1992 bill, diverting the first projects to his own district, then authorizing billions of dollars' worth of additional projects for other members. He was appalled by Smith's selfishness, and House Speaker Hastert was even angrier. Several vulnerable Republicans were counting on environmental infrastructure projects to build support at home before Election Day, and Shaw was counting on CERP, but Smith didn't seem to care who controlled Congress.

Only in Washington could an effort to save taxpayer dollars be considered selfish, but Smith's sudden stand on principle did seem odd. He had agreed to a bill with 138 water projects worth $7 billion, not including the Everglades behemoth, which as far as Shuster concerned was just another huge water project. Smith hadn't objected to flood protection for East Saint Louis or the renourishment of Rehoboth Beach or a comprehensive study of the Merrimack River basin in his home state of New Hampshire. Why was he drawing a line in the sand over sewer projects that actually helped people? Smith was hauled into a meeting with Speaker Hastert, and the avuncular former wrestling coach got as livid as his aides had ever seen him, throwing his pen in Smith's direction. "This is bullshit!" Hastert screamed. But Smith refused to budge. He found it hard to believe that a few sewage plants were going to determine the outcome of the election. "Control of the House is in Bob Smith's hands!" one of his aides wrote in a sarcastic e-mail. "Give me a break."

Congress was running out of time, so Senator Mack went to see House Appropriations Chairman C. W. "Bill" Young of Florida, who agreed to tack CERP onto an agriculture spending bill if the larger Corps bill was scuttled. Shuster realized his entire bill was in danger of stalling without its Everglades engine, so he relented and agreed to pass it without environmental infrastructure. Speaker Hastert then forced Young to tack the infrastructure projects onto a health spending bill. Nobody's ox was going to be gored on Capitol Hill.

It wasn't pretty, but four days before the election, Congress finally passed the Altoonaglades, prompting another round of speeches depicting Clay Shaw as the second coming of Marjory Stoneman Douglas. "Governor Broward, for whom my home county is named, ran on the platform that he was going to drain that swamp, the Everglades," Shaw said. "November 3 is the day we took the first step in really restoring this national treasure."

• • •

Congressman Shaw raced back to south Florida to campaign, and the Everglades headlines helped him edge his Democratic opponent by six hundred votes. Vice President Gore was not so lucky.

Ralph Nader visited Miami for a get-out-the-vote rally on November 5, and used Joe Browder's talking points to blast Gore for "waffling as usual" on the Homestead airport. "Congress and the state of Florida are poised to spend $8 billion to rehabilitate the Everglades," he said. "Why won't the Vice President take a stand against undermining these efforts?" Nader also sent letters to Florida environmentalists, bashing Gore for buckling to real estate interests: "There are no airports situated on the border of national parks in America; the Everglades is the last place to consider changing that."

Gore campaigned in Florida, too, but he never did hold that Everglades rally, and south Florida's environmentalists never did generate much enthusiasm for him. It was frustrating, but Gore always knew that for some Ivory Soap environmentalists, as he put it, "Ninety-nine and forty-four-hundredths percent pure was never good enough." He was more irritated at Mayor Penelas, who was reelected in September, then took off for a vacation in Spain, contributing nothing to Gore's campaign or his fight for a recount. After the votes were counted on Election Day, Gore trailed Bush by 537 votes in Florida. Nader received more than 96,000 votes, and some operatives attributed 10,000 of them to the airport issue. That was more than enough to elect a president who would support oil exploration in the Arctic National Wildlife Refuge, reverse his campaign promise to regulate carbon emissions, and enrage environmentalists like no president since Ronald Reagan. "Oh, I don't think the airport was a major factor in the outcome," Gore said in a recent interview.

Then he paused. "Well, maybe it was."

On December 11, 2000, the Gore campaign's last day in court, Senator Graham woke up in Miami Lakes at 6:05 A.M. According to his characteristically meticulous notebook, he weighed in at 187 pounds, ate some fiber cereal with raisins, and listened to six voice-mail messages. At 9:17 A.M., he flew to Washington on American Airlines flight 1394; he sat in seat 3A, and updated his notebooks for ten minutes at 10:30 A.M. After arriving in Washington, he purchased 11.833 gallons of gas at $1.599 per gallon at a Pennsylvania Avenue Amoco. Then he headed to the White House to celebrate the crowning achievement of his thirty-four-year political career. President Clinton was finally signing the Everglades bill, America's effort to restore Graham's boyhood playground, to re-create the watery wonderland that sheltered millions of wading birds before pioneers like his father began trying to tame it. For Graham, this was bigger than *Bush v. Gore.*

Graham liked to say that when Hamilton Disston first saw the panoramic sawgrass marshes of the Everglades, he must have thought: This doesn't look anything like Philadelphia. It looked strange and unique, and the young industrialist had been determined to convert it into something familiar and productive. But Graham liked strange and unique, as one might expect of a politician who recorded his breakfast choices every morning for posterity. Yes, restoring the Everglades would preserve aquifers and promote ecotourism, but Graham really wanted to restore the Everglades because it was singular, because it distinguished south Florida from other sprawling concatenations of tract homes, strip malls, CVS, and KFC. Marjory Stoneman Douglas had made that point with the first sentence of her book: "There are no other Everglades in the world." It was an American original, it was dying, and now it would receive open-heart surgery. Graham's only concern was that as years passed, billions of dollars were spent, and the patient remained critical, enthusiasm would wane, money would be diverted elsewhere, and the Everglades would be abandoned mid-operation.

Everyone at the bizarre bipartisan White House ceremony knew the Everglades still faced a multitude of threats. There were still 50,000 tons of phosphorus sitting at the bottom of Lake Okeechobee, and 2 million acres of exotic vegetation marching across the Everglades. Red tides were massacring dolphins, manatees, and sea turtles in the estuaries, while plagues and other diseases were killing off the coral reefs. Secretary Babbitt was concerned about the runaway sprawl that continued to chew up the edges of the ecosystem, forcing the Army Corps to paint its restoration masterpiece on an ever-shrinking canvas. Senator Smith threw his arm around Michael Davis, who was moving to Florida to oversee the restoration project, and gestured toward Governor Bush and his aides. "You've got to watch those guys," he whispered to Davis. "They're going to try to grab all that water." President Clinton, shooting the breeze with two legislative aides after the ceremony, flagged another dire threat: rising sea levels. "If we don't do something about climate change," he said, "your Everglades is going to be underwater."

But this was a day to imagine a better future, to reclaim the Everglades in a new way. It was now as unifying a force as it had been during the drainage era, except that the new consensus called for undraining it. While Florida was roiling over "undervotes" and "overvotes," everyone was holding hands over the swamp. "I'd be happy to speculate about the Supreme Court!" Graham told the swarm of reporters gathered outside the West Wing. He then grinned and returned to his preferred subject: "This is a very happy day for the Everglades, and a signal day for the movement around the world to try to repair damaged environmental systems." Smith pointed out that there were no alligators in New Hampshire; the Everglades seemed to transcend state lines, just as it seemed to transcend party lines. It had become a symbol of America's responsibility to make amends to Mother Nature. "We worked together to save a national treasure," Smith said. "It didn't get a lot of ink in what's going on today, but it's very, very important."

The power of the Everglades lay in its example. The twentieth century had been an era of mess-making; the twenty-first century could be a time to clean up the messes. And not just the toxic petrochemical messes that had set rivers on fire and thinned the shells of bald eagles during the sixties, but the ordinary messes created by man's routine dominion over nature. Man's efforts to tame the Everglades had taken a toll—the death tolls of the 1926 and 1928 hurricanes, the near-extinction of panthers and sparrows and gourds, the soil losses and water shortages and traffic jams on the Palmetto Expressway—but they had created homes and vacation destinations for millions of people, and more were on the way. Everglades restoration could set an international standard for sustainable development. It could prove that man and nature could coexist in peace.

After Governor Bush dodged more questions about his brother—"Marvin? He's doing well. That's very kind of you to think about him."—Babbitt stepped forward to talk about the Everglades as a model, a paradigm for thinking on a landscape scale. He suggested a partial list of endangered American ecosystems that could follow south Florida's example: the Great Lakes, San Francisco Bay, New York Harbor, and the Missouri and Mississippi River basins.

Babbitt also mentioned the Louisiana coast, where—due largely to the enduring battle between the Corps and the Mississippi River—wetlands were disappearing at the astonishing rate of twenty-five square miles per year, decimating fish and wildlife while exposing New Orleans to storm surges. Governor Bush predicted that the ripples from the Everglades would extend even further than that: "This is a model—not just for our country, but for projects around the world."

The unanswered question was whether it would turn out to be a new model. Would it be a true restoration project, revamping man's approach to the Everglades, or just another dirt-moving Corps water project, "environmental infrastructure" with better press? Would it inaugurate a new relationship between the human and natural environments in south Florida, encouraging man to limit his footprint and live in harmony with the ecosystem, or would it just facilitate additional growth and sprawl, luring millions more people into the path of the next hurricane? Would politicians and engineers begin to consider the needs of birds, bears, and bays in addition to the needs of man, or would water continue to flow uphill toward money?

On the same day that President Clinton celebrated the new politics of the Everglades at the White House, while the Supreme Court prepared to choose his successor, a meeting in West Palm Beach suggested that the old politics of the Everglades was not quite dead. South Florida was suffering through one of its worst droughts ever, and Lake Okeechobee was so low that the water management district's guidelines prohibited releases for irrigation. But a consultant for the sugar industry had demanded to see the district's engineers, warning in an e-mail that "users will never sit still for zero water-supply releases." He got his meeting on December 11, and with no public input, the engineers agreed to tweak their guidelines so that growers could receive half their usual releases. That winter, the lake plunged below nine feet for the first time in recorded history. A third of the lake disappeared, along with most of its bass, and the region was battered so badly that Governor Bush declared an economic state of emergency. But the sugar industry enjoyed its fourth-largest harvest ever. "Thanks for all your work and for continuing to improve the process," the consultant wrote to the district's engineers.

That money-talks process has damaged the Everglades for more than a century, and it has damaged ecosystems around the world. CERP is supposed to change that, by making sure there is enough water for nature and the public as well as special interests. At a time when fresh water is emerging as the oil of the twenty-first century, Everglades restoration will be a crucial test of man's ability to stave off the bloody water wars that some analysts expect to erupt in the coming decades. If south Florida can't solve problems limited to one state in the wealthiest nation on earth, with billions of dollars to spend and fifty-five annual inches of rain to distribute, it's hard to imagine solving cross-border water disputes in poorer and drier regions. And south Florida has a trump card—the Everglades, the most beloved wetland on the planet, and the most intensely studied. If man can't save the Everglades, what can he save?

Senator Graham is probably the starkest example of the Everglades dilemma. His father was a sugar grower, a cattle rancher, and a real estate developer who dreamed of draining the Everglades. Graham launched the movement to restore the Everglades. But he also continued to support sugar farming, cattle ranching, and real estate development. He wouldn't have been the most popular politician in Florida if he hadn't. In fact, Graham's notes reveal that on the afternoon of December 11, after he watched fifteen minutes of MSNBC commentary about the Supreme Court hearing but before he bought a half-gallon of low-fat milk, the senator spoke to the Cuban-American leader Jorge Mas about the Homestead airport. Graham had declared that he would remain neutral and respect the Clinton administration's final decision, but everyone knew he was still pushing for the airport.

Graham still wanted to save the Everglades; he had started Save Our Everglades. But every politician had to strike a balance between nature and people.

On January 16, 2001, four days before Clinton left office, the administration announced its decision on Homestead. It rejected the airport. It was too late to change the Nader votes of south Florida's environmentalists, but the Everglades had dodged another bullet. It was a reminder that money doesn't always talk. People talk, too. "This is a victory for common sense and public input over special interests," one activist said. It was also a victory for hard-line Ivory Soap environmentalists over the moderates who had considered the airport war a lost cause—although the greenest vice president in history turned out to be a casualty of that war.

As the new millennium dawned, the Everglades was not yet saved. But it was not yet doomed, either. Millions of acres of the ecosystem remained in public ownership. Water quality was improving. And America was now formally committed to restoring the Everglades, with billions of dollars and the prestige of a nation on the line. That didn't mean it would happen, but it meant there was a chance.

Excerpt from *The Everglades: River of Grass*
The Nature of the Everglades

Marjory Stoneman Douglas

There are no other Everglades in the world.

They are, they have always been, one of the unique regions of the earth, remote, never wholly known. Nothing anywhere else is like them: their vast glittering openness, wider than the enormous visible round of the horizon, the racing free saltness and sweetness of their massive winds, under the dazzling blue heights of space. They are unique also in the simplicity, the diversity, the related harmony of the forms of life they enclose. The miracle of the light pours over the green and brown expanse of saw grass and of water, shining and slow-moving below, the grass and water that is the meaning and the central fact of the Everglades of Florida. It is a river of grass.

The great pointed paw of the state of Florida, familiar as the map of North America itself, of which it is the most noticeable appendage, thrusts south, farther south than any other part of the mainland of the United States. Between the shining aquamarine waters of the Gulf of Mexico and the roaring deep-blue waters of the north-surging Gulf Stream, the shaped land points toward Cuba and the Caribbean. It points toward and touches within one degree of the tropics.

More than halfway down that thrusting sea-bound peninsula nearly everyone knows the lake that is like a great hole in that pawing shape, Lake Okeechobee, the second largest body of fresh water, it is always said, "within the confines of the United States." Below that lie the Everglades.

They have been called "the mysterious Everglades" so long that the phrase is a meaningless platitude. For four hundred years after the discovery they seemed more like a fantasy than a simple geographic and historic fact. Even the men who in the later years saw them more clearly could hardly make up their minds what the Everglades were or how they could be described, or what use could be made of them. They were mysterious then. They are mysterious still to everyone by whom their fundamental nature is not understood.

Off and on for those four hundred years the region now called "The Everglades" was described as a series of vast, miasmic swamps, poisonous lagoons, huge dismal marshes without outlet, a rotting, shallow, inland sea, or labyrinths of dark trees hung and looped about with snakes and dripping mosses, malignant with tropical fevers and malarias, evil to the white man.

Even the name, "The Everglades," was given them and printed on a map of Florida within the past hundred years. It is variously interpreted. There were one or two other names we know, which were given them before that, but what sounds the first men had for them, seeing first, centuries and centuries before the discovering white men, those sun-blazing solitudes, we shall never know.

The shores that surround the Everglades were the first on this continent known to white men. The interior was almost the last. They have not yet been entirely mapped.

Spanish mapmakers, who never saw them, printed over the unknown blank space where they lay on those early maps the words "El Laguno del Espiritu Santo." To the early Spanish they were truly mysterious, fabulous with a wealth they were never able to prove.

The English from the Bahamas, charting the Florida coasts in the early seventeen hundreds, had no very clear idea of them. Gerard de Brahm, the surveyor, may have gone up some of the east-coast rivers and stared out on that endless, watery bright expanse, for on his map he called them "River Glades." But on the later English maps "River" becomes "Ever," so it is hard to tell what he intended.

The present name came into general use only after the acquisition of Florida from Spain in 1819 by the United States. The Turner map of 1823 was the first to use the word "Everglades." The fine Ives map of 1858 prints the words separately, "Ever Glades." In the text of the memorial that accompanied the map they were used without capitals, as "ever glades."

The word "glade" is of the oldest English origin. It comes from the Anglo-Saxon "glaed," with the "ae" diphthong, shortened to "glad." It meant "shining" or "bright," perhaps as of water. The same word was used in the Scandinavian languages for "a clear place in the sky, a bright streak or patch of light," as Webster's International Dictionary gives it. It might even first have referred to the great openness of the sky over it, and not to the land at all.

In English for over a thousand years the word "glaed" or "glyde" or "glade" has meant an open green grassy place in the forest. And in America of the English colonies the use was continued to mean stretches of natural pasture, naturally grassy.

But most dictionaries nowadays end a definition of them with the qualifying phrase, "as of the Florida Everglades." So that they have thus become unique in being their own, and only, best definition.

Yet the Indians, who have known the Glades longer and better than any dictionary-making white men, gave them their perfect, and poetic name, which is also true. They called them "Pa-hay-okee," which is the Indian word for "Grassy Water." Today Everglades is one word and yet plural. They are the only Everglades in the world.

Men crossed and recrossed them leaving no trace, so that no one knew men had been there. The few books or pamphlets written about them by Spaniards or surveyors or sportsmen or botanists have not been generally read. Actually, the first accurate studies of Everglades geology, soil, archaeology, even history, are only just now being completed.

The question was at once, where do you begin? Because, when you think of it, history, the recorded time of the earth and of man, is in itself something like a river. To try to present it whole is to find oneself lost in the sense of continuing change. The source can be only the beginning in time and space, and the end is the future and the unknown. What we can know lies somewhere between. The course along which for a little way one proceeds, the changing life, the varying light, must somehow be fixed in a moment clearly, from which one may look before and after and try to comprehend wholeness.

So it is with the Everglades, which have that quality of long existence in their own nature. They were changeless. They are changed.

They were complete before man came to them, and for centuries afterward, when he was only one of those forms which shared, in a finely balanced harmony, the forces and the ancient nature of the place.

Then, when the Everglades were most truly themselves, is the time to begin with them.

II. The Grass

The Everglades begin at Lake Okeechobee.

That is the name later Indians gave the lake, a name almost as recent as the word "Everglades." It means "Big Water." Everybody knows it.

Yet few have any idea of those pale, seemingly illimitable waters. Over the shallows, often less than a foot deep but seven hundred fifty or so square miles in actual area, the winds in one gray swift moment can shatter the reflections of sky and cloud whiteness standing still in that shining, polished, shimmering expanse. A boat can push for hours in a day of white sun through the short, crisp lake waves and there will be nothing to be seen anywhere but the brightness where the color of the water and the color of the sky become one. Men out of sight of land can stand in it up to their armpits and slowly "walk in" their long nets to the waiting boats. An everglade kite and his mate, questing in great solitary circles, rising and dipping and rising again on the wind currents, can look down all day long at the water faintly green with floating water lettuce or marked by thin standing lines of reeds, utter their sharp goat cries, and be seen and heard by no one at all.

There are great shallow islands, all brown reeds or shrubby trees thick in the water. There are masses of water weeds and hyacinths and flags rooted so long they seem solid earth, yet there is nothing but lake bottom to stand on. There the egret and the white ibis and the glossy ibis and the little blue herons in their thousands nested and circled and fed.

A long northeast wind, a "norther," can lash all that still surface to dirty vicious gray and white, over which the rain mists shut down like stained rolls of wool, so that from the eastern sand rim under dripping cypresses or the west ridge with its live oaks, no one would guess that all that waste of empty water stretched there but for the long monotonous wash of waves on unseen marshy shores.

Saw grass reaches up both sides of that lake in great enclosing arms, so that it is correct to say that the Everglades are there also. But south, southeast and southwest, where the lake water slopped and seeped and ran over and under the rock and soil, the greatest mass of the saw grass begins. It stretches as it always has stretched, in one thick enormous curving river of grass, to the very end. This is the Everglades.

It reaches one hundred miles from Lake Okeechobee to the Gulf of Mexico, fifty, sixty, even seventy miles wide. No one has ever fought his way along its full length. Few have ever crossed the northern wilderness of nothing but grass. Down that almost invisible slope the water moves. The grass stands. Where the grass and the water are there is the heart, the current, the meaning of the Everglades.

The grass and the water together make the river as simple as it is unique. There is no other river like it. Yet within that simplicity, enclosed within the river and bordering and intruding on it from each side, there is subtlety and diversity, a crowd of changing forms, of thrusting teeming life. And all that becomes the region of the Everglades.

The truth of the river is the grass. They call it saw grass. Yet in the botanical sense it is not grass at all so much as a fierce, ancient, cutting sedge. It is one of the oldest of the green growing forms in this world.

There are many places in the South where this saw grass, with its sharp central fold and edges set with fine saw teeth like points of glass, this sedge called *Cladium jamaicensis*, exists. But this is the greatest concentration of saw grass in the world. It grows fiercely in the fresh water creeping down below it. When the original saw grass thrust up its spears into the sun, the fierce sun, lord and power and first cause over the Everglades as of all the green world, then the Everglades began. They lie wherever the saw grass extends: 3,500 square miles, hundreds and thousands and millions, of acres, water and saw grass.

The first saw grass, exactly as it grows today, sprang up and lived in the sweet water and the pouring sunlight, and died in it, and from its own dried and decaying tissues and tough fibers bright with silica sprang up more fiercely again. Year after year it grew and was fed by its own brown rotting, taller and denser in the dark soil of its own death. Year after year after year, hundreds after hundreds of years, not so long as any geologic age but long in botanic time, far longer than anyone can be sure of, the saw grass grew. Four thousand years, they say, it must at least have grown like that, six feet, ten feet, twelve feet, even fifteen in places of deepest water. The edged and folded swords bristled around the delicate straight tube of pith that burst into brown flowering. The brown seed, tight enclosed after the manner of sedges, ripened in dense brownness. The seed was dropped and worked down in the water and its own ropelike mat of roots. All that decay of leaves and seed covers and roots was packed deeper year after year by the elbowing upthrust of its own life. Year after year it laid down new layers of virgin muck under the living water.

There are places now where the depth of the muck is equal to the height of the saw grass. When it is uncovered and brought into the sunlight, its stringy and grainy dullness glitters with the myriad unrotted silica points, like glass dust.

At the edges of the Glades, and toward those southern- and southwesternmost reaches where the great estuary or delta of the Glades river takes another form entirely, the saw grass is shorter and more sparse, and the springy, porous muck deposit under it is shallower and thinner. But where the saw grass grows tallest in the deepest muck, there goes the channel of the Glades.

The water winks and flashes here and there among the saw-grass roots, as the clouds are blown across the sun. To try to make one's way among these impenetrable tufts is to be cut off from all air, to be beaten down by the sun and ripped by the grassy saw-toothed edges as one sinks in mud and water over the roots. The dried yellow stuff holds no weight. There is no earthly way to get through the mud or the standing, keen-edged blades that crowd these interminable miles.

Or in the times of high water in the old days, the flood would rise until the highest tops of that sharp grass were like a thin lawn standing out of water as blue as the sky, rippling and wrinkling, linking the pools and spreading and flowing on its true course southward.

A man standing in the center of it, if he could get there, would be as lost in saw grass, as out of sight of anything but saw grass as a man drowning in the middle of Okeechobee—or the Atlantic Ocean, for that matter—would be out of sight of land.

The water moves. The saw grass, pale green to deep-brown ripeness, stands rigid. It is moved only in sluggish rollings by the vast push of the winds across it. Over its endless acres here and there the shadows of the dazzling clouds quicken and slide, purple-brown, plum-brown, mauve-brown, rust-brown, bronze. The bristling, blossoming tops do not bend easily like standing grain. They do not even in their own growth curve all one way but stand in edged clumps, curving against each other, all the massed curving blades making millions of fine arching lines that at a little distance merge to a huge expanse of brown wires or bristles or, farther beyond, to deep-piled plush. At the horizon they become velvet. The line they make is an edge of velvet against the infinite blue, the blue-and-white, the clear fine primrose yellow, the burning brass and crimson, the molten silver, the deepening hyacinth sky.

The clear burning light of the sun pours daylong into the saw grass and is lost there, soaked up, never given back. Only the water flashes and glints. The grass yields nothing.

Nothing less than the smashing power of some hurricane can beat it down. Then one can see, from high up in a plane, where the towering weight and velocity of the hurricane was the strongest and where along the edges of its whorl it turned less and less savagely and left the saw grass standing. Even so, the grass is not flattened in a continuous swath but only here and here and over there, as if the storm bounced or lifted and smashed down again in great hammering strokes or enormous cat-licks.

Only one force can conquer it completely and that is fire. Deep in the layers of muck there are layers of ashes, marks of old fires set by lightning or the early Indians. But in the early days the water always came back and there were long slow years in which the saw grass grew and died, laying down again its tough resilient decay.

This is the saw grass, then, which seems to move as the water moved, in a great thick arc south and southwestward from Okeechobee to the Gulf. There at the last imperceptible incline of the land the saw grass goes along the headwaters of many of those wide, slow, mangrove-bordered fresh-water rivers, like a delta or an estuary into which the salt tides flow and draw back and flow again.

The mangrove becomes a solid barrier there, which by its strong, arched and labyrinthine roots collects the sweepage of the fresh water and the salt and holds back the parent sea. The supple branches, the oily green leaves, set up a barrier against the winds, although the hurricanes prevail easily against them. There the fresh water meets the incoming salt, and is lost.

It may be that the mystery of the Everglades is the saw grass, so simple, so enduring, so hostile. It was the saw grass and the water which divided east coast from west coast and made the central solitudes that held in them the secrets of time, which has moved here so long unmarked.

III. The Water

In the Everglades one is most aware of the superb monotony of saw grass under the world of air. But below that and before it, enclosing and causing it, is the water.

It is poured into Lake Okeechobee from the north and west, from that fine chain of lakes which scatter up and down the center of Florida, like bright beads from a string. They overflow southward. The water is gathered from the northwest through a wide area of open savannas and prairies. It swells the greatest contributing streams, the Kissimmee River, and the Taylor River and Fisheating Creek, and dozens of other smaller named and unnamed creeks or rivulets, and through them moves down into the great lake's tideless blue-misted expanse.

The water comes from the rains. The northern lakes and streams, Okeechobee itself, are only channels and reservoirs and conduits for a surface flow of rain water, fresh from the clouds. A few springs may feed them, but no melting snow water, no mountain freshets, no upgushing from caverns in ancient rock. Here the rain is everything.

Here the rain falls more powerfully and logically than anywhere else upon the temperate mainland of the United States. There are not four sharply marked seasons, as in the North. Here winter and spring and summer and fall blend into each other subtly, with nothing like such extremes of heat and cold. Here, actually, there are only two seasons, the wet and the dry, as there are in the tropics. The rains thunder over all this long land in their appointed season from the low clouds blowing in from the sea, or pour from clouds gathered all morning from the condensation of the wet below. Then for months it will not rain at all, or very little, and the high sun glares over the drying saw grass and the river seems to stand still.

This land, by the maps, is in the temperate zone. But the laws of the rain and of the seasons here are tropic laws.

The men who make maps draw lines across seas and deserts and mountains and equatorial rain forests to show where the Temperate Zone is cut off sharply from the middle equatorial belt. But the sea and the land and the winds do not always recognize that rigidity. Nor do southern Florida and the Everglades.

To the west the map shows the Gulf of Mexico, that warm land-sheltered, almost inland ocean; and from it, moved by the power of the turning world itself, the Gulf Stream pours its warm deep indigo and white-flecked waters north of Cuba and ever northeastward. "The Stream" is a huge swift-running river of warm salt water forced between the Florida coast, which it has shaped, and the Bahama banks, until high up on the blue globe of ocean it swings far across into the gray latitudes, toward frozen seas.

With all that surrounding warm sea water and not forgetting Okeechobee's over seven hundred shallow watery square miles, east forty miles from the sea, and from the Gulf eighty, the whole southern part of Florida might as well be an island. All summer long the trade winds, or winds blowing so steadily nightlong and daylong from the southeast that it makes no difference if weather men quarrel about their being called the true trades, pour across the land their cool stiff tides of ten miles an hour.

Summer and winter its climate is more equable than that of the mainland regions to the north. And because of its average sixty-five inches a year of rainfall on the east coast and sixty-three in the interior of the Everglades, this region actually resembles certain warm and rainy but not too hot tropic lands more than it does those other dry and mountainous countries which lie exactly on the equator. It is a question of the ratio between the temperature and the rainfall and the evaporation. There is an arc at the very tip of Florida, up the lower west coast to Gordon Pass and up the east coast to the Miami and New rivers, which is the only place on the mainland of the United States where tropical and West Indian plants will grow native, because of that warmth and rainfall.

The northern Glades, and Lake Okeechobee, would seem to be in the South Temperate Zone, but the rainfall is subtropic here too.

The rains begin in the spring, in April or even late in May. There may be a few days of stuffy wet heat and brassy sunlight and a great piling up and movement of clouds by the heavy fretful southeast winds. There may be a continuous bumping of thunder far off. The winds that change their compass positions, east to south to west to north to east again, never on the east and south coasts, in any other way but clockwise, are thrashing and uncertain. Then in a sudden chill the rain may shut down in one long slashing burst in which even hailstones may bounce like popcorn against all that darkening land. Then the rain has moved away and the sun flashes again.

Somewhere thereafter it rains over the Glades or the lake for an hour or two every day in switching long bright lines through which the hot sun glistens. Then the marching wet will start again the next day or so, hissing and leaping down in narrow sharply defined paths as the clouds are pushed about here and there in the bright sky. Sometimes the rains may last only a few weeks in May. After that the summer is a long blazing drying time of brilliant sun and trade winds all night under the steady wheeling of the stars. The great piles of vapor from the Gulf Stream, amazing cumulus clouds that soar higher than tropic mountains from their even bases four thousand feet above the horizon, stand in ranked and glistening splendor in those summer nights; twenty thousand feet or more they tower tremendous, cool-pearl, frosty heights, blue-shadowed in the blue-blazing days.

On summer mornings over the Glades the sky is only faintly hazed. The moisture is being drawn up from the sheen among the saw grass. By noon, the first ranks of the clouds will lie at the same height across the world, cottony and growing. The moisture lifts the whipped and glistening heights. The bases darken, grow purple, grow brown. The sun is almost gone. The highest clouds loose their moisture, which is condensed into cloud again before it can reach the earth. Then they grow more heavy. The winds slash before them and the rains roar down, making all the saw grass somber.

Sometimes the rainy season goes on all summer, casually raining here and there so that the green things never quite dry out while salt-water mosquitoes from the brackish pools about the coasts blow on the west wind in thin screaming hordes. When high water in the Glades flows south, the mosquitoes do not breed in it.

But in late August, or perhaps in September, the rainy season sets in in earnest. White-heaped Gulf clouds, colored by afterglows in some tremendous summer sunsets stand like Alps of pure rose and violet and ice-gray against the ultimate blue until they are harried by the more irregular winds. White streamers are blown from their tops, veils from their sides, and they themselves are pushed and scuffled and beaten down into long moving snowy sheets or rolls of gray, yellowish-gray, lavender-gray, greenish-gray—until they smash down in long marching, continuous, reverberating downfalls.

You can see it raining darkly and fiercely far off over there at the horizon across the scorched saw grass. The sky will be a boiling panorama of high and low cloud shapes, cumulus, strato-cumulus, alto-cumulus, dazzling and blue and dun. Sometimes far up, far away, between all that panoply, there will be a glimpse of outer space as green as ice.

Then the lion-colored light shuts down as the rain does, or the clouds fill with their steely haze every outline of the visible world and water falls solid, in sheets, in cascades. When the clouds lift, the long straight rainy lines blow and curve from the sagging underbelly of the sky in steely wires or long trailing veils of wet that glitter in some sudden shaft of light from the forgotten sun.

There will be the smack of cool, almost chilling hard air and the rising sound of long drumming as if the grassy places were hard and dry, or the earth hollow. You hear the tearing swish of the rain on the stiff saw grass as it comes over and beats and goes by slashing its steely whips. There may be short bursts of thunder and veins of lightning cracking the whole sky. They are dwarfed by the power of the rain and the wind.

Below all that the glistening water will be rising, shining like beaten pewter, and the light will lift as if itself relieved of all that weight of the rain. It will change from pewter to silver to pure brightness everywhere. The brownness that has been dullness will be bright tawniness and the reaches and changing forms of the sky will lift higher and higher, lifting the heart. Suddenly all those thousands and thousands of acres of saw grass that have been so lightless and somber will burst into a million million flashes from as many gleaming and trembling drops of wet, flashing back their red and emerald and diamond lights to the revealed glory of the sun in splendor.

Inches of water will have fallen in an hour and still far off the rain will trample below the horizon, undiminished.

In the course of a single day so much rain will fall, as much sometimes as ten or twelve inches, that the glitter of rising water will be everywhere. The blue of the sky is caught down there among the grass stems, in pools stretching and spreading. In a few days of rain, acre after acre of new water will flash in sheets under the sun. Then, as the rain clouds go over every day, the currents will be gathering their small visible courses, streaming and swirling past every grass blade, moving south and again south and by west. Places of open currents have been measured to show a steady running four miles an hour, in the old days, in watercourses and wandering streams among the straight bristle of the saw grass. Sometimes more than half the year's average will have fallen in less than two months.

Meanwhile the rain has been falling far to the northward. Over Okeechobee it has been moved here and there as the steady drive of the trades is changed to fitful inland airs. Thunderstorms roll and reverberate over the surface and lightning marbles the clouds as storms seem to come together from every direction while the greenish and grayish world blinks with acid radiance. The lake may be blotted out by white falling water that sings with a rising note as the surface brims and is beaten. The curtains of rain, the rain fogs, move off or hang and sway in a dirty gray half-light as the descending water smacks on the pitted and broken waves. The world is all water, is drowned in water, chill and pale and clean.

North, still farther up that chain of lakes, the rains fall and brim the fine green-ringed cups. The waters begin again their southward flow. The Kissimmee River is swollen and strongly swirling between its wet marshy banks, but still the water does not move off fast enough. The banks are overflowing and the spongy ground between it and Fisheating Creek is all one swamp. The rains fling their solid shafts of water down the streaming green land, and Okeechobee swells and stirs and creeps south down the unseen tilt of the Glades.

The grass, like all the other growing things after the long terrible dry seasons, begins in the flooding wet its strong sunward push again, from its ropy roots. The spears prick upward, tender green, glass green, bright green, darker green, to spread the blossoms and the fine seeds like brown lace. The grass stays. The fresh river flows.

But even from earliest times, when in the creeping spread of water the grass turned up its swords and made the Everglades, there was too much water in the great lake to carry itself off through the Glades southward. There was nothing but the east and west sandy ridges to hold back the water. To the east from Okeechobee it seeped and was not carried off and stood along an old wandering watercourse soon filled not only with saw grass but reeds and sedges and purple arrowy lilies and floating masses of grass and small trees. That is still called the Loxahatchee Slough. "Hatchee" means "river" in that same Indian tongue which named the lake. "Slough," in south Florida, means any open swampy place which may once have been a tongue of the sea or a river of fresh water, green, watery, flowery country, a place of herons and small fish and dragonflies and blue sky flashing from among the lily pads.

Loxahatchee is pitted with innumerable pools held in by the coastal rock. South of that, from the overflow of the Glades basin itself, the rivers of the east coast run, St. Lucie and the Hillsborough, the New River and Little River and the Miami River, spilling over the rock rim to the tides.

In the same way, west of Lake Okeechobee, at least twice as far from the Gulf, the water spilled and crept out over soggy level lands, half lakes, half swamps, and so into the Caloosahatchee, the left shoulder of the Glades region.

The Caloosahatchee never rose directly in Okeechobee, but in a wide rain-filled funnel of shallow, grassy lakes between Hicpochee and Lake Flirt. Often they dried up and were not there.

West of Lake Flirt, the Caloosahatchee began in earnest, a river so remote, so lovely that even in the days when it was best known it must have been like a dream. It was a river wandering among half-moon banks hung with green dripping trees and enshrouding grapevines, green misted, silent, always meandering. It has that quality of dreaming still, neglected and changed as it is, to this very day.

But in the days of full flood, Caloosahatchee rose and overflowed the flat country for miles, north and south. The water crept and flowed and stood bright under the high water oaks and the cabbage palms, so that a light boat could go anywhere under them. In the clear water all the light under the wet trees was green. Lower down, the more tropic green stood in solid jungles to the reflecting water. The rain water went east and west of the lake, but most strongly along the great course of the Everglades.

Often the rainy season finds its terrible climax in September or October, in the crashing impact of a hurricane, the true cyclonic storm of the tropics. July is not too early to expect hurricanes. In the West Indies they have occurred in June. The old jingle that fishermen recite along these coasts tells the story: "June—too soon. July—stand by. August—look out you must. September—remember. October—all over." Officially in Florida the fifteenth of November closes the hurricane season but farther south these storms occur in November and even in December.

The hurricanes make up, although no man has yet seen the actual beginning of one, as far east as the Azores, where the hot air rises all along the line of the equator as the Northern Hemisphere cools toward winter. Their enormous high-spinning funnels, moving always counterclockwise this north side of the tropic belt, are begun when the rising hot air is flung into circular motion by the immeasurable spinning power of the world. The velocity of that spin around their hollow centers has been recorded as moving as fast as two hundred miles. But generally the recording instruments are blown away before that; so no one knows their greatest speed. Laterally, they creep westward more slowly, ten to forty miles an hour. They enter the Caribbean at some airy rift between those island-mountains rising from the sea, which are often engulfed by them. They may turn northward and eastward through the Mona or the Windward Passage, or across the Cuban coast or through the Bahamas, to drive on southern Florida. They may go howling up these coasts and north along, to show the Temperate Zone what the roused raging power of the tropics can be like.

Smaller but intense and dangerous hurricanes spring up sometimes in the late fall in the Yucatan channel and thrash the Gulf of Mexico and harry the Texas or Florida coast. They attack the Glades from there. Later still, they become more freakish and unpredictable, like maelstroms of wind gone wild.

But as the northern winter creeps downward, the hurricane season is slowly conquered. The towering clouds of summer are leveled to mild sheets and rolls of gleaming stuff, widespread, dappled and mackereled, or with the great silvery brushings of mares'-tails. Often there are no clouds at all toward the zenith, which has lost its summer intensity of violet and burns now with the bright crisp blue of northern autumns. Then the air is fresh and sweet.

This is the dry season. Officially, no rain should fall. Yet there have been wet, chill winters in which the rains have come down on the edge of a northern cold front while the east winds go around south and west and north, and stand there for three days of cold, or die utterly so that the frost drifts into the low places and at first sun the hoar-rimmed leaves grow black.

In the winter dry season, there takes place here another and gentler phenomenon of the equatorial tropics. In a windless dawn, in some light winter ground fogs, in mists that stand over the Everglades watercourses, the dew creeps like heavy rain down the shining heavy leaves, drips from the saw-grass edges, and stands among the coarse blossoming sedges and the tall ferns. Under the tree branches it is a steady soft drop, drop and drip, all night long. In the first sunlight the dew, a miracle of freshness, stands on every leaf and wall and petal, in the finest of tiny patterns, in bold patterns of wide-strung cobwebs; like pearls in a silvery melting frostwork. The slant yellow sun of winter dries it up in the next hour but all the secret roots are nourished by it in the dry ground.

Then toward what the North would call spring, dryness creeps again over the land, with the high-standing sun. Between one day and the next the winds grow new and powerful. In the Glades the water shrinks below the grass roots. In open muddy places far south the surface dries and cracks like the cracks in old china, and where some alligator has hitched his slow armored length from one drying water hole to another the pattern of his sharp toes and heavy dragging belly in the marl is baked hard.

The saw grass stands drying to old gold and rustling faintly, ready, if there is a spark anywhere, to burst into those boiling red flames which crackle even at a great distance like a vast frying pan, giving off rolling clouds of heavy cream-colored smoke, shadowed with mauve by day and by night mile-high pillars of roily tangerine and orange light. The fires move crackling outward as the winds blow them, black widening rings where slow embers burn and smolder down into the fibrous masses of the thousand-year-old peat.

Then the spring rains put out the fires with their light moving tread, like the tread of the running deer, and the year of rainy season and of dry season has made its round again.

"Look where the sun draws up water," people say of those long shafts of brightness between clouds. The saw grass and all those acres of green growing things draw up the water within their cells and use it and breathe it out again, invisibly. Transpiration and evaporation, it is called; an unending usage of all the water that has fallen and that flows. Sixty per cent of it, over half of all those tons and tons of water which fall in any rainy season, is taken up again. Dried up. The air is fresh with it, or humid, if it is warm. But in the middle of the Glades in the full heat of summer the condensation is so great that the air is cooled and the temperature lowered half a degree with every two miles or so inland. It is not so much the cool movement of wind as standing coolness, freshness without salt, wetness that is sweet with the breath of hidden tiny blossoming things luminous in the darkness under the height and white magnificence of the stars. Such coolness is a secret that the deep Glades hold.

On the west coast there are land breezes and sea breezes. West-flowing winds often sweep out of those cooling Glades down the slow mangrove rivers and out to the islands on the coasts, rivers of coolness among warm and standing airs.

With all this, it is the subtle ratio between rainfall and evaporation that is the final secret of water in the Glades. We must know a great deal more about that ratio and its effect on temperature in all this region to understand its influence on the weather, on frosts and winds and storms.

All this has been caused by other cycles dictated by remote and terrible occurrences beyond this infinitesimal world, the cyclones of heat and shadow that pass across the utter fire of the sun. Or other laws of a universe only half guessed at. Those majestic affairs reach here in long cycles of alternating wet and dry. There have been years after years of long rainy seasons when the Glades indeed were a running river, more water than grass. Or, more recently, cycles of drought, when there is never enough rain to equal the evaporation and transpiration and the runoff.

Because of all this, the high rate of water usage as against the natural runoff, it is clear that rainfall alone could not have maintained the persistent fine balance between wet and dry that has created and kept the Everglades, the long heart of this long land. If Okeechobee and the lakes and marshes north that contribute to it, if rivers and swamps and ponds had not existed to hoard all that excess water in a great series of reservoirs by which the flow was constantly checked and regulated, there would have been no Everglades. The whole system was like a set of scales on which the forces of the seasons, of the sun and the rains, the winds, the hurricanes, and the dewfalls, were balanced so that the life of the vast grass and all its encompassed and neighbor forms were kept secure.

Below all that, holding all that, the foundation stuff of this world, lies the rock.

IV. The Rock

To understand the Everglades one must first understand the rock.

The outline of this Florida end-of-land, within the Gulf of Mexico, the shallows of the Bay of Florida and the Gulf Stream, is like a long pointed spoon. That is the visible shape of the rock that holds up out of the surrounding sea water the long channel of the Everglades and their borders. The rock holds the fresh water and the grass and all those other shapes and forms of air-loving life only a little way out of the salt water, as a full spoon lowered into a full cup holds two liquids separate, within that thread of rim. Lower the tip of the spoon a very little and the higher liquid moves out across the submerged end, as the water does at the end of the Glades.

The rock beneath Okeechobee is only a few feet above sea level. The surface of the lake is only twenty-one feet above the level of the salt water. The surface rock below the Everglades dips south at an incline of half a foot to every six miles. The rim of rock that retains it is narrower and higher on the east coast, but in the west it is hardly visible as a rim at all. There it is a broad space of inland swamps and prairies and coastal sandy land and salt-invaded marshes. Yet both hold against the sea.

The rock is not by any means the oldest in the world. It is nothing like the perdurable granite of the ancient Appalachian spine of the eastern continent. The material of it came from the sea. Out of reach of air it is lumpy, soft, permeable limestone, grayish white, unformed. They call it "oölitic limestone" because it is no more fused together than a lot of fish eggs. In the sun and air it hardens in clumps and shapeless masses, dark, or gray, or yellowish, all full of holes, pitted and pocked like lumps of rotting honeycomb. In itself it shows no foldings or stratification, but holds streaks of sand or shells or pockets of humus.

West and east of Okeechobee the rock just below the surface is not so much oölitic limestone as a shelly, marly sandstone. To the east it underlies the Loxahatchee Slough. To the west, under the swamps and flat ponds beyond Okeechobee, the Caloosahatchee ran strong after the rains, turning from bank to bank in its overflow, carving its way across and into that sandstone plain in the meanders which are the habit of much older rivers. The Caloosahatchee is not so old as that river of Troy which was first called "Meander," but in her curvings and turnings she cut down through new sand into older and older layers of rock and of pure shell fossils. Some of the greatest layers of fossil shells in the world were cut into and crumbled, and cut into again as every year Caloosahatchee changed her banks.

In spite of what the early scientists believed, and people still repeat incorrectly to this day, this lower Florida is not an old coral reef. It is oölitic limestone, with broken bits of staghorn coral or shapes of brain coral embedded in it. "Miami limestone," they call it.

The fresh water from Okeechobee moving south on the long course of the Everglades has in these thousands of years worn the soft rock in a broad longitudinally grooved valley. Along the east coast the rock rim may be seen in long south-curving ledges, worn by the action of the sea. The rock rims emerge farther south still as beaches and peninsulas beyond half-enclosed salt rivers and broad opening bays. East, the sunken reefs stretch to the abrupt edge of the Gulf Stream itself, where the brilliant lime-green, surfless shallows drop off into the blue, deep surge.

South of the last peninsula, which makes Biscayne Bay, the ridges stretch below water to make the long spiny curves of the Florida Keys, turning southwest as the Gulf Stream came, all the way to Key West and the last Tortugas. Other lesser known rims of rock curve within the southeast mainland in a line of high rocky islands. These are called the Everglades Keys. They became legendary. The early white people believed they contained caves into which all the Indians disappeared before hurricanes, warned by the "blossoming of the saw grass," as if the saw grass did not blossom every year, and as if the broken ledges of rock in these inland keys could hide anything except ferns and coral snakes and roots.

On the east coast, the rivers from the great main saw-grass stream broke through the rock rim in a series of low waterfalls or rapids. The rock stood as a constant natural dam between the fresh water of the Glades and the heavier invading tidal salt, which in dry times creeps up the bottoms of the rivers and would destroy all living fresh-water forms above the mangrove line.

The St. Lucie and the rivers running into Jupiter Inlet and the Mouth of the Rat, the Hillsborough, the New River with its two branches, Little River and Arch Creek, had their shallow falls. The Miami River from the Everglades brawled over twenty-five feet of rapids in the North Fork, with a fall of over six feet. Snapper Creek had its ferny, rocky dam, above which the fresh-water springs bubbled clear through all the higher rock.

The water of all these rivers was clean and clear, perhaps faintly brown from mangroves, but with no Everglades humus in it to stain the bright sand bottoms. The water of the bays was clear, tinted by the light shimmering in water over sand reefs, and sea gardens, and acres of clean green weed.

All that rocky barrier in fact was threaded with springs. All these rivers were known to the early sailors as "sweet water rivers," not a name but a description. The springs bubbled up and filled the great ancient pot holes in the rock which the sea had whirled into and worn smooth and deserted, thousands of years before.

The limestone tips very gently downward to the south until at the end it disappears below the surface and is overlaid by a fine, white calcareous marl that muffles all the shallow water of the Bay of Florida. There are blown sand beaches at Cape Sable, the French word for "sand." There are deposits of leafy humus here and there over the marly meadows, and brackish lakes are set like mirrors among the mangroves, and the wandering watercourses are more salt than fresh. It is a marl laid down by infinitesimal algae. There are bits of seashells in it, bleached by the sun and abraded by the tides. The ripple shadows in the marly water are blue, in a liquid like thin cream. To wade out into it is to sink to the hips in ooze, in faintly scratchy white mud, warm as warm milk in the sun-warmed sea water over it.

All this end of the peninsula is a country that the sea has conquered and has never left. Beyond, westward, it is a pattern of curved shapes solid with mangroves cut out by salt water. There, from Cape Sable northward again to the lonely point of Cape Romano, lie the Ten Thousand Islands. They are the sunken tops of sand dunes the winds and the hurricanes piled up from the shallower Gulf. The mangrove covered them. They are edged on the west by fine, hard white sand beaches that are changed in shape with every hurricane. The passes become filled with sand that the mangroves and salt shrubs hurry to make solid, and then new passes are cut swiftly where the driven salt water rages.

On this coast, south of Cape Romano, the rivers move silent and enormous from the saw grass to the mangrove, and so to the sea, linked by innumerable streams and cuts and channels, utterly bewildering, never completely known. The freshwater Turner River comes down from pineland and cypress to a dozen channels among mangroves, and so to Chokoloskee Bay. Chatham Bend opens out of Chevalier Bay like a great inland brackish lake. Some rivers above the tides are fresh water from the Everglades, many channeled and intricate; Lostman's River with its sand bars into the Gulf and Rodger's River and Harney's River. Then with impressive opening and far inward reaching among saw-grass plains, there is the Broad River known only to the multitudinous flights of the birds at sunrise and sunset, crammed with fish, and once boiling with crocodiles; at noons it lies glaring, soundless, solitary, untouched. South of that is Shark River carved in the rock, and the Little Shark in all their branchings and windings among mangroves, opening inland in channels that lead behind the three capes of Cape Sable, more inlets than rivers, lakes, lagoons, all sun struck, sea invaded.

For the retaining shape of the rock that holds in the western curve
of the saw-grass river, one has to go back to the cape and the angle
that Caloosahatchee makes with it, a rough right angle, subtended
by the long line of the outer coast. Up in that angle, as if it was the
western armpit of that country, there is an unseen dome of limestone
which makes a watershed for all this. It is not the edge of the true
Glades, but it shows where the rock lies nearest to the surface, about
at the place now called Immokalee. Water in the rains runs north to
Caloosahatchee, west to the seacoast, in some of those small rivers
like the Estero and the Imperial, once called Surveyor's Creek, and the
Corkscrew River, and into Trafford Lake and Deep Lake, and others.
Blue water stands in deep, round cups of the rock. East lies a strange
country that borders the Glades sharply. The northern part is called
the Devil's Garden, a broken scrubby open land. South is the mass of
the Big Cypress, by which for a long time the saw grass curves.

All this again is drained by a bright green swampy, grassy trough
called the Okaloacochee Slough, which leads southwestward into the
Fakahatchee Swamp, half salt marshes and fresh water, which leads
in turn into Fakahatchee Bay behind the mounded islands above the
Allen, now the Barron, River.

So, in the middle of the narrow east coast and the broader west
coast, the Everglades curve grandly in the limestone.

The rock is still strange stuff. The fresh Glades water wore it
horizontally from north to southwest in a long valley, never smooth, but
a series of long uneven ridges and troughs that hold the muck and the
southernmost marl. It was porous stuff to begin with. And then all that
fresh water wore and seeped down into it through the cloaking vegetable
decay, charged with the strong organic acids that ate and gnawed and
dissolved chemically the penetrable limestone. The acid water worked
and tunneled it, so that it is honeycombed and fretted and pocked, under
the layers of the muck, into something very like rocky sponge. All but
the hardest cores and spines of limestone were eaten out downward
many feet below the surface in an infinity of grooved strange shapes.

If all the saw grass and the peat was burned away there would be exposed to the sun glare the weirdest country in the world, thousands and hundreds of thousands of acres of fantastic rockwork, whity gray and yellow, streaked and blackened, pinnacles and domes and warped pyramids and crumbling columns and stalagmites, ridgy arches and half-exposed horizontal caverns, long downward cracks, and a million extraordinary chimney pots. Under the sun glare or the moonlight it would look stranger than a blasted volcano crater, or a landscape of the dead and eroded moon.

Nothing of that limestone shows above the surface in the northernmost Glades. For sixty miles or so south of Lake Okeechobee the river of the saw grass sweeps wider than the horizon, nothing but saw grass utterly level to the eye, a vast unbroken monotony. The grass crowds all across the visible width and rondure of the earth, like close-fitting fur. Clouds and the smoke of fires stand far off and are sunk in it, like the smoke of ships at sea. This is the Everglades at their greatest concentration, a world of nothing but saw grass. Nothing seems to live here but a few insects, hawks working a few acres, buzzards soaring against the piled snow of a cloud, a heron flying its far solitary line.

The saw grass sweeps about halfway south, where the whole course begins to arc a little to the westward. There the muck is not so deep, less solidly packed over the limestone. The hardest rock began to show at the surface its ridged top in hundreds and thousands of places. In times of drought the soil subsided around this rock which the new rains and the suns eroded and wore off level. And the surface water around the exposed rock under the surrounding grass shaped and pointed it in the direction of the currents in islands like anchored ships swinging all in the same direction, fleets, flotillas, armadas of stranded island shapes. Southward the islands crowd more thickly in the thinning muck.

Plants seized upon these rocks, hardly less avidly than the saw grass, carried by wind or birds or water, and needing only a pinch of humus, some cranny more hospitable than the all-choking saw grass, in which to send down their first threadlike roots. The enormous machinery of the sun drew up the sprouts, the stalks, the trunks of trees, the covering leaves. Every island, almost at once, reached a tropical struggling life in blossom and quick seed.

These islands are, like the saw grass, the particular feature of the Glades. Small or great jungles, they loom out of the brownness of the saw grass in humped solid shapes, like green whales and gray-green hangars and domes and green clouds on the horizon. They look like hummocks, and many books persist in calling them so. They are called also "heads" and "strands" and "tree islands," but the right name is "hammock," from "hamaca," an Arawak word for jungle or masses of vegetation floating in a tropical river. These are the hammocks of the sawgrass river. No man has explored all of them, or could. They are too many. From north to south there is a changing vegetation on them, by which they can be characterized. Some have known history such as men make. Some hide marks of deeds that few men remember. Some have not known one single human thing, only the beasts and snakes and birds and insects that know nothing else since their time began.

That is not all, for this rock has a shape greater than this visible one of the peninsula. Westward it makes a great shadowy sunken plateau extending far out into the Gulf of Mexico in shallows that drop off abruptly into the midmost deeps. On the east coast it is gouged deeply by a stream of warm water over one of cold, with a current greater than the Mississippi that separates the American continent here at Florida from the Bahama Banks, two hundred fathoms deep, moving four to five miles an hour. It is the enormous oceanic river of the Gulf Stream.

The whole structure of this rock is known as the Floridian plateau. Still, to understand it, one must know how it was made, in time's forward-pushing inexorable years.

V. The River of Time

The life and death of the saw grass is only a moment of that flow in which time, the vastest river, carries us and all life forward. The water is timeless, forever new and eternal. Only the rock, which time shaped and will outlast, records unimaginable ages.

Yet, as time goes, this limestone is recent. The earth itself is so much older that time grows faint about it, in those hundreds of millions of years which, in its cooling and wrinkling and rising and wearing and changing, might have been but a single day. The mind of man has no way of holding so vast a concept. He has devised symbols to spare himself the agony of trying to think what that awfulness was like.

The earth was shrunken and old, the continents almost as we know them, already split and re-formed and taking shape within the all-encompassing ocean, when the Floridian plateau was still a part of the floor of a warm, tranquil, equatorial sea. The Appalachian Mountains to the north already had been thrust up and worn down again by the friction of centuries and still the sea lay here, wrinkling and glittering in its moon-enchanted tides. There was a stump at the south of that continental mass like the beginning of north Florida. Or perhaps it was an island. But that was all.

There came one last heaving and changing, some huge undersea faulting and pinching up, and in long slow centuries the Floridian plateau rose a little, only a little, the east edge of it a little higher, the west sloping back gradually to the sea again. The sea water ran off it as if it were the rising shoulder of some huge sleek beast. The ridged shelly oozy bottom of the sea broke into the sunlight for the first time and as the waters within what we now call the Gulf of Mexico felt the narrowing pinch of the land, they began to pour out irresistibly, as the earth turned, in the Gulf Stream.

They say that was late in the earth's history, a mere geologic yesterday. The Pliocene, they call it, which is only a way of bunching together an unbelievable section of centuries in one word that can be handled without too much thought. They think it was nineteen million years ago and that the period lasted millions of years.

Life had taken shape on the earth long before, long, long before, the top of this Florida rock rose above the sea. Shapes of growing things which this land still bears in the Everglades and the coasts are so much older than the region itself that thought grows dizzy contemplating them.

Eight hundred million years ago there were growing on the warm lands then far north palmlike plants called cycads. They grow on the borders of the Everglades now. The ants were already fixed in their selfless habits of busyness, as they are today. The first reptiles, shaped like the small green lizards on the sun-warmed stones, had taken to the air and learned to fly, having changed their scales to wings, one hundred and fifty-five million years before there was any Florida at all.

The little scorpions that crawl out of rotted wood on cold nights and hang on a wall like perfect small lobsters, whose species have the longest history of any air-breathing thing, are older than any of this rock of which the Floridian world is made. The sponges, the corals, the shellfish, some of the crabs along these coasts, the tiniest shell forms that turn up in the muck below the oldest saw grass, are older than the whole shape of this land. There are forms among these hammocks more ancient by a hundred million years. The most recent dragonfly that crawls from its larval state to dry and stretch its glistening fine wings on the tallest saw grass was shaped and formed so many centuries before the whole contour of the Everglades began that one looks from the insect to the wideness of this grassy world with a feeling that understanding of permanence is, like an understanding of time itself, impossible.

Only yesterday, then, they say, the Floridian plateau was lifted up, long after the quails and the swifts and the flamingos, the warblers and the water snakes, the owls, the woodpeckers and the alligators had assumed their present forms and habits.

The north of Florida may have been a part of the north mainland before the West Indian islands rose in the fire of their own volcanoes from the edge of a huge fault in the ocean bottom that skirts the inmost deeps. The questing shadows of sharks ranged freely throughout all the oceans, east to west, before Central America was an isthmus. There were monkeys in the world and gibbons and that brooding incalculable new thing in the other continent, this shambling figure with the spark under his thick skull that was the beginning of all thought—man. The Everglades were not begun before him.

But in that farthest age of the recent they call the Miocene, when the shape of the Florida plateau was forced up out of the sea, it was the last such rising movement, or so most of the scientists think, that occurred here.

There are no loopings and foldings of this rock, no tilted broken strata here. There is only, far below the surface, the evidence of that old, old first movement, a slow, smooth, regularly marked ancient dome. The top of the dome, the anticline, is highest north of Okeechobee, near the center of north Florida at Ocala. From Ocala southward, like the slopes of a deep-hidden hill, the strata flow downward, farther and farther below. The oldest, the Cretaceous, which first existed one hundred twenty million years ago, is the lowest, sweeping down ten thousand feet below the southern rim of the Everglades and of the sea. The Eocene lies above that and the Oligocene above that, and the Miocene curves from north to south under Okeechobee and the Everglades from ninety to nine hundred feet below the surface. The surface itself, this oölitic limestone, lies from the surface to ninety feet down under the southern mangrove rim.

All those strata, from the dome at Ocala, sweep down and farther down in regular flowing layers. So that what is on the surface in north Florida, the water-bearing rock that makes the lovely north Florida springs and cavernous rivers "measureless to man," is hidden under the Everglades by a thousand feet. From that rock nothing reaches up to the surface here. That is why only the surface rain water that flows into Okeechobee makes the Everglades and seeps into and frets the rock. There are no upgushings from deep subterranean rivers.

It proves again that, since the Miocene, those nineteen million years ago, there has been no change in the larger shape of the Floridian plateau itself. What happened, to surface that hidden dome with limestone and sand and marl and muck and peat, was the phenomenon of the polar ice.

Ice that had formed at the poles, in a world then tropic almost to what we now call the Arctic Circle, in an age of warmth began to move slowly downward in enormous encroaching glaciers, huge mile-high cliffs of ice that scraped and tore and gouged away rocks and mountains in their courses and sucked up water from all the oceans as they froze, in a slowly chilling world. Perhaps the mountains had been thrust up too high, so that too much snow had fallen. Perhaps there was less sunlight, from the tornadoes of shadow that pass across the surface of the sun itself.

At least, the scientists are sure of the ice. It moved southward, in the Northern Hemisphere, killing the forests, shoving the changing forms of living things all southward, scarring and grinding the face of the world. It never reached Florida.

Then, after an interminable cold and shadowy time, the warmth came back. The glacial polar ice melted and retreated, and all that released water flowed back into the seas. The sea rose up over the edges of that new shape of the Floridian plateau, warming and washing it gently, moving north of Okeechobee in a long curve over the once-risen land.

Four times in that measureless age of ice the glaciers froze and formed again and crept grating and jarring southward, in the fogs and glacial mists, beyond the Great Lakes and New York State and New England. Again freezing, they drew up the waters of the earthly seas. When they melted and left the deep gouged lakes and the ice-worn rounded hills and the glacial moraines, they gave back the waters to the sea again. But in some places there had been faultings and enlargings in the ocean's undersurface, and huge lakes were left filled with water so that each time the sea rose back over lower Florida it never reached its earlier levels. Each time the curving waterline was lower.

Okeechobee was left then as a great inland fresh-water lake, a swampy amorphous depression. From this, the powerful rains leached away the salt. On the east coast the lines of retaining ridges were left as they may be seen today, all parallel, north and south but each lower, as between the glacial stages the sea each time did not stand so high.

The slow retreating waves dropped their silt between the great glacial periods. Below the waterline there was water erosion, holes in the shoreward rocks smooth scoured by the sand and the tides. The marl at the south accumulated softly. The fresh-water limestone was established. By the lines of shell fossils geologists can today trace the old sea levels. A last glacier took up the water and the sea shrank back and the fresh water from Okeechobee flowed out and down the slow incline. The western rivers swept farther out along the soft rock than they do now, dropping the scoured silt and sand in outer peninsulas and bars and wind-swept dunes for the sea to shape.

Then that last glacier melted and retreated farther north than it ever had before. It is there now, the north polar icecap, the glaciers, the ice fields of the arctic, the thick ice over Greenland and inner Alaska and northern Siberia. Not all the water was returned to the sea. But there was enough to change again the changing shape of lower Florida. The sea crept back up the mouths of the western rivers, filling and submerging the outer shape of Caloosahatchee, creeping up toward the Everglades in all those shapeless, spreading, wandering tidal rivers among the mangroves, filling up the sand dunes so that they became the Ten Thousand Islands.

On the east coast, along that highest rim of rock, the south-swinging current that edges between the Gulf Stream and the land laid down sand in bars and peninsulas, filled up some of the mouths of rivers like the Loxahatchee, and laid the sand again along the ridgy shapes of the keys. On the south the sea crept over the marly shallows and kept the currents between the keys open, and they filled the Bay of Florida, and laid down the sand of Cape Sable and worked the standing salt ponds and lagoons of the Everglades delta shore.

The sea had risen. It is there now. The shape of this land was established. The long flow of time seems to have slowed to its humdrum working of day to day. Yet if this is the end of the ice age, or if the sea is still rising and the ice melting, if there will be other ages of ice and sunlessness when the seas are taken up and the moist hidden caverns of the lower deeps again revealed, who can guess? Time never stops.

So down the valley of the Glades the fresh water crept in its recent shape, recent by centuries unrecorded except for the rock. The saw grass, one of the oldest forms of green life on the already aged earth, thrust up here its first sharp, resilient spears.

After it, in the earth now seeming so long established, the forms old and new of plant and animal and insect life hurried to take their hold.

Time moves again for the Everglades, not in ages and in centuries, but as man knows it, in hours and days, the small events of his own lifetime, who was among the last of the living forms to invade its shores.

VI. Life on the Rock

The saw grass and the water made the Everglades both simple and unique. Yet bordering and encroaching on that simplicity, fighting for foothold on its coasts and islands, a diversity of life lives upon the rock that holds it. The saw grass in its essential harshness supports little else. It repelled man. But on the rock the crowding forms made life abundant, so that between the two the chronicle is balanced.

One begins with the plants.

If the saw grass here is four thousand years old, many other of these plant associations may have been here almost as long.

In the time of which I write, toward the end of the past century when everything was as it had been, the southern vague watery rim of Okeechobee was bordered by a strange jungle. The crusted wave foam was washed down among windrows of dead reeds and branches and rotting fish. In that decay a wide band of jungle trees sprang up.

Southwest it was all custard apple, a subtropic, rough-barked, inconspicuous tree, with small pointed leaves and soft fruits. It grew fiercely, crowded on roots that became gnarled trunks or trunks twisted and arched into bracing roots in the drag of the water. The spilth and decay of the custard apple, the guano of crowds of birds that fed on them, whitening the leaves, built up in the watery sunlessness below them an area of rich black peat, denser than muck, two or three miles wide and six or eight feet deep.

The earliest Americans on the lake called this area "the custard apple bottoms." It was edged with tall leather ferns and Boston ferns and knotted with vines, which no man could get through without axes or dynamite. Lake water crept darkly below.

The southeast was edged with a less tropical jungle, scrub willow with its light-green pointed leaves and yellow catkins and the ropy brown bark of elderberries, bearing out of their lacy plates of white blossoms the purple-black fruit about which the blue jays and the mockingbirds, the great black-glinting Florida crows, the grackles and the red-winged blackbirds in their thousands set up a flapping and creaking and crowing and ker-eeing. Bees and bright flies and yellow butterflies hovered when the blossoms were sweet. Under their shadows ground rattlers moved sluggishly. Winds carried to them from the reedy lake clouds of feeble white insects lake people call "chizzle winks," which breed and die in myriads in a short few days.

These were the willow-and-elder bottoms, which fought shrewdly with the saw grass for every rocky space. The dark-brown peaty muck they left went east up the lake edge between the sand ridges and the saw-grass arms.

Over all this thick jungle region climbed and hung down in moving green curtains the heart-shaped leaves of moonvines. In the luminous unseen dark of the night the moonflowers opened acres after acres of flat white blossoms, cloud white, foam white, and still. Northward, lake water moved darkly under the tiny pointed reflections of the stars. Below the region the moonflowers and the moon made their own, with no man's eye to see them, moved the enormous darkness without light of the saw-grass river.

East along the curving Everglades borders and west by the farther coast stood everywhere in their endless ranks the great companies of the pines. Where they grew the rock was highest—"high pine land," people called it. Their ranks went off across an open slough in a feathery cliff, a rampart of trunks red-brown in the setting sun, bearing tops like a long streamer of green smoke. Their warm piny breaths blew in the sun along the salt winds. They covered here, as they did everywhere in Florida, interminable miles.

Some southern longleaf, "common yellow pine," with its taller trunk and bushier branches is scattered south from the Caloosahatchee and down the east coast to the New River. But below there, wherever it could find foothold in high rock, and up behind the western mangrove to what is now Gordon Pass, which is the area of West Indian vegetation, grows the Caribbean pine. It stands everywhere about the borders of the Caribbean. It is called slash pine. But in Dade County from the first it was called Dade County pine.

Its trunks are set thick with rust and brown and grayish bark patches, which resist fire. The patterns of its skimpy branches people find strange, or beautiful. Dying alone, as they often do away from their great companies, killed by lightning or the borer that instantly finds injured bark, these pines stand dead a long time, rigid gray or silver, their gestures frozen. The young fluffy pines start up everywhere about them, bearing long pale candles in the new light of spring.

With the Caribbean pines, as they do with other pines of the South, always grow the palmettos. These are saw palmettos, silver-green, blue-green, or in dry times magnificent tawny-gold across vast open savannas. Their spiky fans cover all the ground beneath the pine trees, on unseen spiny trunks. If they are burned, with a great oily popping and seething, only the blackened trunks are left, writhing like heavy snakes.

The small brown Florida deer step neatly at the edge of pine forests like these. The brown wildcats know them. The clear light falls mottled through the branches faintly green over endless fan points. Inconspicuous wild flowers grow in the wiry grass between palmettos, faint blue chicory, or yellow tea bush, or the tiny wild poinsettias with their small brush strokes of scarlet. The quail pipe and their new-hatched young run like mice with their small cheeping, at the edge of such pineland, and the brown marsh rabbit with small ears and no apparent tail nibbles some bit of leaf.

A diamondback rattlesnake may push out here slowly after such a rabbit or the cotton mice, or lie after shedding his flaky old skin to sun the brilliant dark lozenge marks on his almost yellowish new scales, slow to coil or rattle unless angered. Then in a blur he draws back in quick angles that wide-jawed head with the high nose balanced over the coils, his slitted eyes fixed and following his object, the forked tongue flicking through the closed jaws, tasting the disturbed air. His raised tail shakes the dry rattle of its horny bells. His strength, his anger, engorges that thick muscular body, ruffles his barky scales. If he strikes it is at one-third of his length. The jaws open back so that the long fangs strike forward and deep. His recovery is quicker than the eye can see. Or he lifts tall that kingly head before he lowers it in retreat, holding himself grandly, with the same dignity that has made him the king among all these beasts.

All the woodpeckers in south Florida yank and hitch and cluck and rap their way up these great patched pine trunks, all with red heads, the downy, the hairy, the red-bellied, and that diabolical creature with a red and white and black head like a medieval battle-ax, the pileated, which the early settlers called so truly "the Lord God Almighty." But in those early days the even more impressive ivory-billed, which we shall never see again, startled these pinewoods with his masterly riveting.

Even in the middle of the saw-grass river, where an outcrop of old rock is the only evidence of preglacial times, the pines grow tall to show where the rock lies. The buzzards and the black vultures, their ragged wing tips like brush strokes of India ink, sail and sail and rise on the upcurrents and soar in their pure flight, turning about some old roost they have always kept and returned to year after year. Their piercing glances watch for the glint of flies' wings over carrion they crave, the most valuable birds in the world. Or from the muddy water holes about the pineland the brown-black water moccasins slide their wet ridged scales. Startled, they coil to retract those open, white-lined jaws, like a queer white flower to anything peering down. Death is there too.

Where the pines are thin, the Indians found their first source of life. There grow foot-tall, ferny green cycads, plants older than this rock, with yellow and orange cones for flowers and great thick roots. This is the "coontie" of the oldest Indian legend. Its root is grated and squeezed and sifted to flour to make the thick watery gruel "sofkee," which was always the basis of the Indians' diet here. The Indians' legend came partly from the Spanish fathers. They say that once there was a great famine here in Florida. The Indians prayed to the Master of Breath, who sent down His Son, God's Little Boy, to walk about at the edge of the pinelands and the Glades. And wherever He walked, there in His heel marks grew the coontie, for the Indians to eat and reverence.

Sometimes it is called compte. The early white men learned of it and grated it to make starch and knew it as arrowroot. By the pinelands north of the Miami River, the Indians camped often, so that their women could gather it in what was called the Coontie grounds.

The dragonflies on iridescent wings dart and hang in squadrons by the open air of pinelands. Below among the grass roots stirs all the minute dustlike activity of the ants.

In the summer hosts of big red-and-yellow grasshoppers, with heads shaped like horses', will descend and eat holes in all the softer leaves. Walking sticks fly like boomerangs. Shining brown leaf-shaped palmetto bugs scurry like cockroaches. Spiders like tiny crabs hang in stout webs. The birds snap at small moths and butterflies of every kind. A blue racer, the snake that moves across the cleared sand like a whiplash, will with one flick destroy the smooth, careful cup of the ant lion in the hot sand. The whole world of the pines and of the rocks hums and glistens and stings with life.

But if, on these rocky outcrops, the pines and the palmettos were destroyed, by lightning or the old fires of Indians, another great tree took its place and gradually changed, with its own associated forms, the whole nature of the place. This was the live oak, the first of the hardwoods. They made the first hammocks at the edge of rivers or on the driest Everglades islands.

The warblers in their thousands migrate up and down the continents, spring and fall, South America to North America and back, enlivening the oaks with their small flitting shapes and tiny whisperings; palm and pine warblers, the myrtles, the black-throated blues, the amazing redstarts, the black-and-whites—oh, it is impossible to name all the warblers that pass here.

Dozens of other birds are there in their seasons in the live oaks, among the red splashes of air plants and the patches of lichens. Green lizards puff out their throats like thin red bubbles in some unhearable love call. The eternal cardinals raise their first trillings before dawn, "Pretty, pretty, pretty—sweet, sweet-sweet." A mocking bird, all one whirl of gray and white, flips through those aging branches chasing a small brown owl or flinging him in the sun from the topmost twigs to fling up his modulated lovely spray of words. The small tree-frogs pipe there in the gray before rain and the yellow-billed cuckoo croaks, and the almost invisible rain-crow. In the first tender dark the little owl comes out from his hole where the mocker chased him to begin his low, liquid bubbling, the velvet secret voice of the night.

South in the lower hammocks in a live oak, frowsy with dry Resurrection ferns that the first rain startles to green life, some pale green slender stalk with minute gold eyes will seem to grow along a branch, poking upward on its own thoroughfare, high and higher in the leafiness, a small green tree snake. Such little snakes achieve the sun among the topmost leaves to be spied on by one of the loveliest bird-shapes of all, the free-flying, easy-soaring, easy-turning swallow-tailed kite, that lifts and ranges and swings in whiteness above the tree-tops. One stoop and the free bird slides upward on the wind, dangling the small tender green thing in pure sunlight to its airy and exalted death.

A huge ancient line of live oaks stands along the westernmost rock edge of Okeechobee, deep with moss, looking out over miles and miles of shallow reeds between them and the mirage-like glitter of that inland sea. There in open, sunblasted country the black-and-white caracara, that the Mexicans take for their national eagle, cries harshly from a bush top, his round, gold glance avid for lizards on the ground. A king snake, brave in yellow and fine black in the dust, snaps back in zigzags the speed of his fighting body. Grackles in thousands, creaking their interminable wheels of sound, hang in the reeds their thousands of pouchlike nests. Life is everywhere here too, infinite and divisible.

The live oaks, like dim giants crowded and choked by a thrusting forest of younger hardwoods, made that great Miami hammock, the largest tropical jungle on the North American mainland, which spread south of the Miami River like a dark cloud along that crumbling, spring-fed ledge of rock. Here where the leaf-screened light falls only in moving spots and speckles to the rotting, leaf-choking mold, the hoary ruins of live oaks are clouded by vines and resurrection ferns, their roots deep in the rotting limestone shelves among wet potholes green-shadowed with the richest fern life in the world— maidenhair and Boston ferns and brackens and ferns innumerable. At night the mosquitoes shrill in the inky blackness prickled through with fireflies.

About the live oaks is waged the central drama of all this jungle, the silent, fighting, creeping struggle for sunlight of the strangler fig. It is one of those great trees people call rubber trees or Banyans. They are all *Ficus*, but the strangler is *Ficus aurea*. A strangler seed dropped by a bird in a cranny of oak bark will sprout and send down fine brown root hairs that dangle and lengthen until they touch the ground. There they grip and thicken and become buttresses. Over the small hard oak leaves the thick dark-green oily strangler's leaves lift and shut out the sun. Its long columnar trunks and octopus roots wrap as if they were melted and poured about the parent trunk, flowing upward and downward in wooden nets and baskets and flutings and enlacings, until later the strangler will stand like a cathedral about a fragment of tree it has killed, crowning leaves and vast branches supported by columns and vaultings and pilings of its bowery roots.

The stranglers are only the most evident and dramatic of all these crowding tropical jungle trees; smooth red-brown gumbo limbos, ilex, eugenias, satinwoods, mastic, cherry laurel, paradise trees, the poisonous manchineel, the poisonwood, the Florida boxwood and hundreds more which the hurricanes brought over from Cuba and the West Indies.

This was the jungle that people thought the Everglades resembled. Buds flit through it only rarely. The little striped skunk leaves its trail. The brilliant coral snake buries its deadly black nose in its loam. The false coral, the harlequin, with its yellow nose, is hardly less hidden. Spiders stretch their exquisite traps for pale insects. Small brown scorpions move on the rotting logs. And far up among the tufted air plants the small native orchids are as brown and pale yellow and faint white as the light they seek.

Everywhere among these branches moves imperceptibly one of the loveliest life forms of these coasts—the pale-ivory, pale-coral, pale-yellow and pale-rose, whorled and etched and banded shell of the *Liguus*, the tree snails. Their pointed shell bubbles are found chiefly on smooth-barked trees in the dry hammocks, but every Everglades island-hammock has its own varieties, subspecies developed in countless lifetimes in a single unique area, varying with an infinity of delicate differences. They came from the tropics. They are a world in themselves.

Moths move in and out of the light at the jungle edge, the twilight hawk moth, seeking the pale-flowered vines, and the rose-colored tiger moth. There is a day in the spring when myriads of white butterflies drift over the whole land, moving out to sea inexplicably. They are caught and die in thousands against the jungles.

But here especially the strangest of the butterflies quivers silently in the bands of sun in the green light of leaves, the only one of its tropical kind on this mainland. It is the *Heliconius*, named for the sun, barred black and pale yellow as the light and shade, wavering always in companies, which no bird will touch. The *Heliconius* drowse of nights in colonies, delicately crowded and hanging on a single small tree. When bright moon light reaches them they have been seen to wake and drift about, filling a leafy glade with their quivering moon-colored half-sleep.

About the rivers of the west, north of the tropic vegetation line, grows the water oak. The water oaks grow taller and more regular than the live oaks. Their longer pointed leaves drop off the bare boughs in a brief winter and put on their new light green long before the rusty live oaks renew themselves, in that misty river country. Both crowd down to the glossy water and make landscapes like old dim pictures where the deer came down delicately and the cows stand, to drink among their own reflections.

In the great Miami hammock, along the banks of almost every river, bordering the salt marshes, scattered in the thinner pineland, making their own shapely and recognizable island-hammocks within the Everglades river, everywhere, actually, except in the densest growth of the saw grass itself, stands the Sabal palmetto. To distinguish it from the low shrubby saw palmetto, it is called the cabbage palm. With its gray-green fans glittering like metal in the brilliance, its round top bearing also branches of queer blossoms and hard dark berries, the cabbage palm grows singly or in dramatic clumps over stout round trunks. The basketwork of old fan hilts is broken off below as the trunk grows tall and smooth. Ferns and vines and air plants and lizards and spiders live in that basketwork. They are often engulfed by strangler figs. They bristle on the banks of fresh-water rivers among the oaks. They make dense islands in the saw-grass river.

They are a northern growth, unrelated to the tropical palms, to the coconut palms that rise above the outer beaches and are set everywhere in cities, or the great royal palms that tower among the Everglades keys and in a few magnificent hammocks of their own toward the west coast. The Spaniards introduced the coconuts to Panama from the Philippines, the royals are native West Indians. Their nuts were blown over from Cuba and germinated in the rain-washed debris of some tropical cyclone. Other delicate palms, like the silver palm of the lower mainland, came the same way.

Then there is the enduring cypress. There are many cypresses in the world but the Everglades region has two: the short, often dwarf, pond cypress and the tall fresh-water river cypress. It is the river cypress that is tall, to 125 feet, silver gray, columnar, almost pyramidal on its broad fluted base, whose curiously short branches lose their leaves in winter and stand ghostly and gaunt among the hanging Spanish moss and red-tongued air plants. Spring draws out from the ancient wood the tiny scratched lines of its thready leaves, the palest yellow-green darkening to emerald. It is a fine timber tree. White and green, over brown water, against an amazing blue and white sky, it is most strangely beautiful.

The cypress that grows in muddy water has that curious acompaniment, the rootlike extension into the air, like dead stumps, called cypress knees, which are thought to aerate the mudbound roots. The dry-land cypress does not need them. It grows up rivers of both coasts and about the lake. But in its greatest area, a vast dramatic association of river cypress and pond cypress marks the west bank of the saw-grass river, and forms the Big Cypress Swamp.

The Big Cypress extends south from the Devil's Garden, a wilderness of pine and scrubby stuff and bushes, near that dome of land in the angle of Caloosahatchee and the lake, south in great fingers which reach to the headwaters of the Turner River, as far down as the salt water and the mangrove. The rock below it is uneven and ridgy, all hollows and higher places. It is called "swamp" because in the rains the water stands in it and does not run off. It is not moving water, like the saw-grass Glades. It was called "the Big Cypress" because it covered so great an area.

The river cypresses stand there in wintertime in great gray-scratched heads, like small hills, towering above the dense and lower pond, or dwarf, cypress between, thinly set in the wetter hollows of wire grass,

starred with white spider lilies and sedges and, in drier places, milkwort
in saffron-headed swaths. Red-shouldered hawks cruise the low cypress
and the marshlands, marsh hawks balance and tip, showing white rump
marks, and far over at the edge of a thicket a deer feeds, and flicks his
white-edged tail before he lifts his head and stares.

From high in a plane at that time of year the Big Cypress seems an
undulating misted surface full of peaks and gray valleys changing to
feathering green. East of it, sharply defined as a river from its banks,
move the vast reaches of the saw grass.

The brown deer, the pale-colored lithe beautiful panthers that
feed on them, the tuft-eared wildcats with their high-angled hind legs,
the opossum and the rats and the rabbits have lived in and around
it and the Devil's Garden and the higher pinelands to the west since
this world began. The quail pipe and call through the open spaces.
The great barred owls hoot far off in the nights and the chuck-will's-
widows on the edge of the pines aspirate their long whistling echoing
cries. The bronze turkeys, the most intelligent of all the birds or
beasts, feed in the watery places and roost early in the thick cypress
tops, far from the prowlers below. And the black Florida bear, which
sleeps even here his short winter sleep, goes rooting and grumbling
and shoving through the underbrush, ripping up logs for grubs and
tearing at berries, scorning no mice.

The bears move to the beaches and, like the panthers, dig for turtle
eggs. They catch crabs and chew them solemnly and eat birds' eggs if
they find them, and ripe beach plums. The panthers prey most on the
range hogs of the settlers, and so they are hunted with dogs, and fight
viciously, killing many before they leap into trees and, snarling, never
to be tamed, are shot.

Here in the cypress pools—but for that matter, everywhere in the
watery Glades, from lake to sea—lives the Glades' first citizen, the otter.
Like the birds, he is everywhere. The oily fur of his long lithe body is
ready for heat or cold, so long as it is wet. His webbed hands are more
cunning than the raccoon's. His broad jolly muzzle explores everything,

tests everything, knows everything. His quickness is a snake's lightning quickness. He has a snake's suppleness and recovery, but not the snake's timidity. His heart is stout and nothing stops him.

The otter has been seen to swim and flirt and turn among a crowd of thrashing alligators, from whose clumsy attack he has only to dive and flash away. He knows how to enjoy life in the sun better than all the rest of all the creatures. He is gay. He is crammed with lively spirit. He makes a mud slide down a bank, and teaches his cubs to fling themselves down it and romp and tumble and swim upside down in the frothing water. He is fond of his female and plays with a ball and has fun. His ready grinning curiosity and friendliness betray him to the hunter and trapper. This is his home.

On the scanty dwarf cypress the gray Ward's heron stands rigid. The big black-and-white wood ibis, like a stork, which flies so high and so far in such grave and orderly squadrons, slides downward on hollow wing and lights with a great flapping and balancing that makes the tree look silly under its teetering grip as it stares down its great curved beak for a frog there below. It is as though all the life of the Everglades region, every form of beast or bird or gnat or garfish in the pools, or the invisible life that pulses in the scum on the pools, was concentrated in the Big Cypress.

The dwarf cypress has its area, perhaps the most fantastic of all, far toward Cape Sable, south of the live-oak jungle that was called Paradise Key, where the royal palms stood high overhead like bursting beacons seen across the sloughs. Men have said they have seen panthers here, not tan, but inky black. There southward, under the even more brilliant light, as if already the clouds reflected the glare from the sea beyond, the small cypress, four or five feet tall, stands in the rock itself, barely etched with green. These trees seem centuries old, and they are very old indeed, in spite of fire and hurricane. Even in full leaf their green is scant. There are moccasins around their roots out of the standing clear water, and high, high over, a bald eagle lazily lifting, or an osprey beating up from the fishing flats.

Lake jungles, pine, live oak, cabbage palmetto, cypress, each has its region and its associated life. As the islands in the saw grass pointed southward in the water currents, their vegetation changes like their banks, from temperate to subtropic, to the full crammed tropic of the south.

The northernmost are dense with pond apple or willow and elder and those charming border shrubs, the silver myrtle, with its spring flowering of silky silvery pompons, the day jasmine, with the dark berries the mocking birds clamor for, salt bush, bay, and dozens of others. There are hammocks centered about live oaks or cabbage palms, crowded and screened with bushes. There are cypress hammocks hung with moss over a deep brown pool where a single heron waits and the blue flag and the water hyacinth and the green arrowy lilies catch a great shaft of light. Beyond lies all that broad, open, windy level of the Glades.

So, at the end of the saw-grass river and its bordering coasts, begins the mangrove. It shows itself in short tufts first, in green leggy rosettes far south where the saw grass is shorter over thinner muck and the emerging rock. There are higher hammocks of mangrove beyond. The saw-grass river goes on around them. In the rainy seasons the current is visible, rippling and bending the grass tops as it flows nearer the sea. The draining fresh-water rivers begin far above the highest salt tides.

Glaring under the sun or bleak in the rain, flat, with patches of scrub and bright salt weeds, this is the country of the birds. The man-o'-war birds from the keys float and tumble over it in their effortless flight. Thousands of sandpipers and sanderlings rise in clouds from the water meadows. The ducks paddle in every stream end. In some great inland bay of salt water, two or three hundred white pelicans, like a snowbank on a reef, wait for the tide to drive the small fish into their scooping beak-pouches. They are ten feet from wing tip to wing tip. When they rise, fraying out, peeling off, in a slow roar of aroused wings, they float high up and sail and turn in great concentric circles, white against cloud dazzle.

The headwaters of these fresh-water rivers are covered in the season with the stick nests of herons, the least blue and the glossy and the Louisiana and the solitary great white heron, the stalker of these shallows. The roseate spoonbills, with their queer bills and delicate, flame-stained pink feathers, have gone through their ridiculous stick courtships here. And drifting down from the saw-grass reaches come the white ibis, in a huge sweeping, turning, flashing circle, tilted groundward so that the lower birds stop and stand with outstretched necks before they are caught up again in the wheeling flying, the rare pattern of their nuptial flight.

Like the otter, raccoons are everywhere about the Everglades, but here in the south by the mangrove they have lived in thousands. Their wonderful small black fingers find the crawfish and the sea grape and the coon oysters hanging on the mangrove roots. They stand on their hindquarters with their hands on their furry chests to snuff at every wind with those sharp curious noses, peering at everything strange with those black-masked bright eyes.

Within the salt meadows here at the end of this world, green with thick-stemmed waterweeds glowing yellow and coral about the white marly water, the round-nosed dark alligators find their way along fresh-water inland streams, after their fierce matings, to make their nests.

There must be heat and wetness for the porous thirty or more eggs the female alligator lays. She works together a great mass of waterweeds or grass, mashing it down and letting it rot and grow compact, and brings new stuff in her toothy jaws to pile on it. When it is settled and steaming she pushes the top off and makes a hole and lays her eggs and covers them again. It may take eight weeks or more, with the sun heat and the ferment and the moisture, to incubate them.

When the young squeak in their shells she comes back and pushes the stuff from off their lively tails and bright eyes and tiny jaws, ready, direct from the shell, to snap at minnows.

But the crocodile, the narrow-jawed, clay-colored faster beast, goes no farther inland than the warm beaches to dig a hole in dry sand and lay dozens of eggs that any moisture may destroy. Their clay-colored slitted eyes watch unblinking among the mangrove-stained watercourses, vicious, intractable, and vanishing. This last is their country.

So, fringing the salt marshes or the higher saw-grass meadows of the southeast, where the deer make their paths, there begins in earnest the dark mangrove wilderness. It is a world as monotonous, as unique, as the saw grass. It looks as if there was nothing here but mangroves and the mud stinking with vegetable rot and saltreek and the moving sea water.

Mangroves exist in many places in the tropics. But this area is the most magnificent mangrove forest, and the greatest, in the American hemisphere.

Two kinds of mangroves dominate this association, the black and the red. It begins on the last peat with tall hammocks and forests of buttonwoods, called "white mangrove," not a true mangrove at all but *Conocarpus*. Then in the first level of the high tide stands deep-rooted the black mangrove, the *Avicennia nitida*, not tall, but thick, which often sends from its submerged roots up through two or three feet of mud and water the curious pneumatophores, like thousands of sharp bristling sticks, most difficult to wade through. They are breathing organs. The darkgreen leaves above them often exude salt crystals. The roots stain the water brown with strong tannin.

Beyond that, marching out into the tides low or high, and rooted deep below them in marl over the rock, goes the great *Rhizophora*, the red mangrove, on its thousands of acres of entwined, buttressed and bracing gray arches. The huge trunks, often seven feet in circumference, stand as high as eighty feet here, one hundred in the drier spots. Their canopy of green obliterates the sky. In the shadowy light over that world of arches over water all is clear gloom.

Entering wave ridges are beaten down, here. The foam washes in all the flotsam of the sea, the accumulated drift of the shallows. The thick leaves turn yellow continually and continually fall. The decay rises among those arches and the younger growths slowly march seaward across it, holding and building the land.

From the high branches long hairy ropes swing and hang down to reach the water and branch into roots. Some have few fruits. Some are heavy with long seeds like small thin torpedoes, which fall and stick in the mud under low tide and grow. But more commonly they float and are carried endlessly on sea currents that bring them upright and alive, ready to root, on other far mangroveless tropic shores.

Where these mangroves came from, to this young mud over the older rock, cannot be guessed. This may be one of the great parent forests from which seeds have been carried as far as the South Pacific. Nobody knows.

The mangrove here is at least as old as the Everglades, of which it marks the end.

Excerpt from *Silent Spring*
A Fable for Tomorrow

Rachel Carson

There was once a town in the heart of America where all life seemed to live in harmony with its surroundings. The town lay in the midst of a checkerboard of prosperous farms, with fields of grain and hillsides of orchards where, in spring, white clouds of bloom drifted above the green fields. In autumn, oak and maple and birch set up a blaze of color that flamed and flickered across a backdrop of pines. Then foxes barked in the hills and deer silently crossed the fields, half hidden in the mists of the fall mornings.

Along the roads, laurel, viburnum and alder, great ferns and wildflowers delighted the traveler's eye through much of the year. Even in winter the roadsides were places of beauty, where countless birds came to feed on the berries and on the seed heads of the dried weeds rising above the snow. The countryside was, in fact, famous for the abundance and variety of its bird life, and when the flood of migrants was pouring through in spring and fall people traveled from great distances to observe them. Others came to fish the streams, which flowed clear and cold out of the hills and contained shady pools where trout lay. So it had been from the days many years ago when the first settlers raised their houses, sank their wells, and built their barns.

Then a strange blight crept over the area and everything began to change. Some evil spell had settled on the community: mysterious maladies swept the flocks of chickens, the cattle and sheep sickened and died. Everywhere was a shadow of death. The farmers spoke of much illness among their families. In the town the doctors had become more and more puzzled by new kinds of sickness appearing among their patients. There had been several sudden and unexplained deaths, not only among adults but even among children, who would be stricken suddenly while at play and die within a few hours.

There was a strange stillness. The birds, for example—where had they gone? Many people spoke of them, puzzled and disturbed. The feeding stations in the backyards were deserted. The few birds seen anywhere were moribund; they trembled violently and could not fly. It was a spring without voices. On the mornings that had once throbbed with the dawn chorus of robins, catbirds, doves, jays, wrens, and scores of other bird voices there was now no sound; only silence lay over the fields and woods and marsh.

On the farms the hens brooded, but no chicks hatched. The farmers complained that they were unable to raise any pigs—the litters were small and the young survived only a few days. The apple trees were coming into bloom but no bees droned among the blossoms, so there was no pollination and there would be no fruit.

The roadsides, once so attractive, were now lined with browned and withered vegetation as though swept by fire. These, too, were silent, deserted by all living things. Even the streams were now lifeless. Anglers no longer visited them, for all the fish had died.

In the gutters under the eaves and between the shingles of the roofs, a white granular powder still showed a few patches; some weeks before it had fallen like snow upon the roofs and the lawns, the fields and streams.

No witchcraft, no enemy action had silenced the rebirth of new life in this stricken world. The people had done it themselves.

This town does not actually exist, but it might easily have a thousand counterparts in America or elsewhere in the world. I know of no community that has experienced all the misfortunes I describe. Yet every one of these disasters has actually happened somewhere, and many real communities have already suffered a substantial number of them. A grim specter has crept upon us almost unnoticed, and this imagined tragedy may easily become a stark reality we all shall know.

What has already silenced the voices of spring in countless towns in America? This book is an attempt to explain.

Excerpt from *Silent Spring*
The Obligation to Endure

Rachel Carson

The history of life on earth has been a history of interaction between living things and their surroundings. To a large extent, the physical form and the habits of the earth's vegetation and its animal life have been molded by the environment. Considering the whole span of earthly time, the opposite effect, in which life actually modifies its surroundings, has been relatively slight. Only within the moment of time represented by the present century has one species—man—acquired significant power to alter the nature of his world.

During the past quarter century this power has not only increased to one of disturbing magnitude but it has changed in character. The most alarming of all man's assaults upon the environment is the contamination of air, earth, rivers, and sea with dangerous and even lethal materials. This pollution is for the most part irrecoverable; the chain of evil it initiates not only in the world that must support life but in living tissues is for the most part irreversible. In this now universal contamination of the environment, chemicals are the sinister and little-recognized partners of radiation in changing the very nature of the world—the very nature of its life. Strontium 90, released through nuclear explosions into the air, comes to earth in rain or drifts down as fallout, lodges in soil, enters into the grass or corn or wheat grown there, and in time takes up its abode in the bones of a human being, there to remain until his death. Similarly, chemicals sprayed on croplands or forests or gardens lie long in soil, entering into living organisms, passing from one to another in a chain of poisoning and death. Or they pass mysteriously by underground streams until they emerge and, through the alchemy of air and sunlight, combine into new forms that kill vegetation, sicken cattle, and work unknown harm on those who drink from once pure wells. As Albert Schweitzer has said, "Man can hardly even recognize the devils of his own creation."

It took hundreds of millions of years to produce the life that now inhabits the earth—eons of time in which that developing and evolving and diversifying life reached a state of adjustment and balance with its surroundings. The environment, rigorously shaping and directing the life it supported, contained elements that were hostile as well as supporting. Certain rocks gave out dangerous radiation; even within the light of the sun, from which all life draws its energy, there were short-wave radiations with power to injure. Given time—time not in years but in millennia—life adjusts, and a balance has been reached. For time is the essential ingredient; but in the modern world there is no time.

The rapidity of change and the speed with which new situations are created follow the impetuous and heedless pace of man rather than the deliberate pace of nature. Radiation is no longer merely the background radiation of rocks, the bombardment of cosmic rays, the ultraviolet of the sun that have existed before there was any life on earth; radiation is now the unnatural creation of man's tampering with the atom. The chemicals to which life is asked to make its adjustment are no longer merely the calcium and silica and copper and all the rest of the minerals washed out of the rocks and carried in rivers to the sea; they are the synthetic creations of man's inventive mind, brewed in his laboratories, and having no counterparts in nature.

To adjust to these chemicals would require time on the scale that is nature's; it would require not merely the years of a man's life but the life of generations. And even this, were it by some miracle possible, would be futile, for the new chemicals come from our laboratories in an endless stream; almost five hundred annually find their way into actual use in the United States alone. The figure is staggering and its implications are not easily grasped—500 new chemicals to which the bodies of men and animals are required somehow to adapt each year, chemicals totally outside the limits of biologic experience.

Among them are many that are used in man's war against nature. Since the mid-1940's over 200 basic chemicals have been created for use in killing insects, weeds, rodents, and other organisms described in the modern vernacular as "pests"; and they are sold under several thousand different brand names.

These sprays, dusts, and aerosols are now applied almost universally to farms, gardens, forests, and homes—nonselective chemicals that have the power to kill every insect, the "good" and the "bad," to still the song of birds and the leaping of fish in the streams, to coat the leaves with a deadly film, and to linger on in soil—all this though the intended target may be a few weeds or insects. Can anyone believe it is possible to lay down such a barrage of poisons on the surface of the earth without making it unfit for all life? They should not be called "insecticides," but "biocides."

The whole process of spraying seems caught up in an endless spiral. Since DDT was released for civilian use, a process of escalation has been going on in which ever more toxic materials must be found. This has happened because insects, in a triumphant vindication of Darwin's principle of the survival of the fittest, have evolved super races immune to the particular insecticide used, hence a deadlier one has always to be developed—and then a deadlier one than that. It has happened also because, for reasons to be described later, destructive insects often undergo a "flareback," or resurgence, after spraying, in numbers greater than before. Thus the chemical war is never won, and all life is caught in its violent crossfire.

Along with the possibility of the extinction of mankind by nuclear war, the central problem of our age has therefore become the contamination of man's total environment with such substances of incredible potential for harm—substances that accumulate in the tissues of plants and animals and even penetrate the germ cells to shatter or alter the very material of heredity upon which the shape of the future depends.

Some would-be architects of our future look toward a time when it will be possible to alter the human germ plasm by design. But we may easily be doing so now by inadvertence, for many chemicals, like radiation, bring about gene mutations. It is ironic to think that man might determine his own future by something so seemingly trivial as the choice of an insect spray.

All this has been risked for what? Future historians may well be amazed by our distorted sense of proportion. How could intelligent beings seek to control a few unwanted species by a method that contaminated the entire environment and brought the threat of disease and death even to their own kind? Yet this is precisely what we have done. We have done it, moreover, for reasons that collapse the moment we examine them. We are told that the enormous and expanding use of pesticides is necessary to maintain farm production. Yet is our real problem not one of *overproduction*? Our farms, despite measures to remove acreages from production and to pay farmers *not* to produce, have yielded such a staggering excess of crops that the American taxpayer in 1962 is paying out more than one billion dollars a year as the total carrying cost of the surplus-food storage program. And is the situation helped when one branch of the Agriculture Department tries to reduce production while another states, as it did in 1958, "It is believed generally that reduction of crop acreages under provisions of the Soil Bank will stimulate interest in use of chemicals to obtain maximum production on the land retained in crops."

All this is not to say there is no insect problem and no need of control. I am saying, rather, that control must be geared to realities, not to mythical situations, and that the methods employed must be such that they do not destroy us along with the insects.

The problem whose attempted solution has brought such a train of disaster in its wake is an accompaniment of our modern way of life. Long before the age of man, insects inhabited the earth—a group of extraordinarily varied and adaptable beings. Over the course of time since man's advent, a small percentage of the more than half a million species of insects have come into conflict with human welfare in two principal ways: as competitors for the food supply and as carriers of human disease.

Disease-carrying insects become important where human beings are crowded together, especially under conditions where sanitation is poor, as in time of natural disaster or war or in situations of extreme poverty and deprivation. Then control of some sort becomes necessary. It is a sobering fact, however, as we shall presently see, that the method of massive chemical control has had only limited success, and also threatens to worsen the very conditions it is intended to curb.

Under primitive agricultural conditions the farmer had few insect problems. These arose with the intensification of agriculture — the devotion of immense acreages to a single crop. Such a system set the stage for explosive increases in specific insect populations. Single-crop farming does not take advantage of the principles by which nature works; it is agriculture as an engineer might conceive it to be. Nature has introduced great variety into the landscape, but man has displayed a passion for simplifying it. Thus he undoes the built-in checks and balances by which nature holds the species within bounds. One important natural check is a limit on the amount of suitable habitat for each species. Obviously then, an insect that lives on wheat can build up its population to much higher levels on a farm devoted to wheat than on one in which wheat is intermingled with other crops to which the insect is not adapted.

The same thing happens in other situations. A generation or more ago, the towns of large areas of the United States lined their streets with the noble elm tree. Now the beauty they hopefully created is threatened with complete destruction as disease sweeps through the elms, carried by a beetle that would have only limited chance to build up large populations and to spread from tree to tree if the elms were only occasional trees in a richly diversified planting.

Another factor in the modern insect problem is one that must be viewed against a background of geologic and human history: the spreading of thousands of different kinds of organisms from their native homes to invade new territories. This worldwide migration has been studied and graphically described by the British ecologist Charles Elton in his recent book *The Ecology of Invasions*. During the Cretaceous Period, some hundred million years ago, flooding seas cut many land bridges between continents and living things found themselves confined in what Elton calls "colossal separate nature reserves." There, isolated from others of their kind, they developed many new species. When some of the land masses were joined again, about 15 million years ago, these species began to move out into new territories—a movement that is not only still in progress but is now receiving considerable assistance from man.

The importation of plants is the primary agent in the modern spread of species, for animals have almost invariably gone along with the plants, quarantine being a comparatively recent and not completely effective innovation. The United States Office of Plant Introduction alone has introduced almost 200,000 species and varieties of plants from all over the world. Nearly half of the 180 or so major insect enemies of plants in the United States are accidental imports from abroad, and most of them have come as hitchhikers on plants.

In new territory, out of reach of the restraining hand of the natural enemies that kept down its numbers in its native land, an invading plant or animal is able to become enormously abundant. Thus it is no accident that our most troublesome insects are introduced species.

These invasions, both the naturally occurring and those dependent on human assistance, are likely to continue indefinitely. Quarantine and massive chemical campaigns are only extremely expensive ways of buying time. We are faced, according to Dr. Elton, "with a life-and-death need not just to find new technological means of suppressing this plant or that animal"; instead we need the basic knowledge of animal populations and their relations to their surroundings that will "promote an even balance and damp down the explosive power of outbreaks and new invasions."

Much of the necessary knowledge is now available but we do not use it. We train ecologists in our universities and even employ them in our governmental agencies but we seldom take their advice. We allow the chemical death rain to fall as though there were no alternative, whereas in fact there are many, and our ingenuity could soon discover many more if given opportunity.

Have we fallen into a mesmerized state that makes us accept as inevitable that which is inferior or detrimental, as though having lost the will or the vision to demand that which is good? Such thinking, in the words of the ecologist Paul Shepard, "idealizes life with only its head out of water, inches above the limits of toleration of the corruption of its own environment . . . Why should we tolerate a diet of weak poisons, a home in insipid surroundings, a circle of acquaintances who are not quite our enemies, the noise of motors with just enough relief to prevent insanity? Who would want to live in a world which is just not quite fatal?"

Yet such a world is pressed upon us. The crusade to create a chemically sterile, insect-free world seems to have engendered a fanatic zeal on the part of many specialists and most of the so-called control agencies. On every hand there is evidence that those engaged in spraying operations exercise a ruthless power. "The regulatory entomologists . . . function as prosecutor, judge and jury, tax assessor and collector and sheriff to enforce their own orders," said Connecticut entomologist Neely Turner. The most flagrant abuses go unchecked in both state and federal agencies.

It is not my contention that chemical insecticides must never be used. I do contend that we have put poisonous and biologically potent chemicals indiscriminately into the hands of persons largely or wholly ignorant of their potentials for harm. We have subjected enormous numbers of people to contact with these poisons, without their consent and often without their knowledge. If the Bill of Rights contains no guarantee that a citizen shall be secure against lethal poisons distributed either by private individuals or by public officials, it is surely only because our forefathers, despite their considerable wisdom and foresight, could conceive of no such problem.

I contend, furthermore, that we have allowed these chemicals to be used with little or no advance investigation of their effect on soil, water, wildlife, and man himself. Future generations are unlikely to condone our lack of prudent concern for the integrity of the natural world that supports all life.

There is still very limited awareness of the nature of the threat. This is an era of specialists, each of whom sees his own problem and is unaware of or intolerant of the larger frame into which it fits. It is also an era dominated by industry, in which the right to make a dollar at whatever cost is seldom challenged. When the public protests, confronted with some obvious evidence of damaging results of pesticide applications, it is fed little tranquilizing pills of half truth. We urgently need an end to these false assurances, to the sugar coating of unpalatable facts. It is the public that is being asked to assume the risks that the insect controllers calculate. The public must decide whether it wishes to continue on the present road, and it can do so only when in full possession of the facts. In the words of Jean Rostand, "The obligation to endure gives us the right to know."

Excerpt from *Hope for Animals and Their World*

Healing Earth's Scars:
It's Never Too Late

Jane Goodall, Gail Hudson, and Thane Maynard

Throughout the pages of this book, we have shared stories of species that, although rescued from the brink of extinction, are still endangered by lack of suitable habitat in the wild. Tropical and old-growth forests, woodlands and wetlands, prairies and grasslands, moorlands and deserts—all landscapes—are disappearing at a terrifying rate.

So how, people ask, can I have hope for the future? Indeed, I am often accused of being unrealistically optimistic. What is the point of saving endangered life-forms, people ask, if there is nowhere for them to live except in zoos? So let me share why it is that, against all odds, I have hope for the animals and their world. Why it is I believe that human know-how and the resilience of nature, combined with the energy and commitment of dedicated individuals, can restore damaged environments so that, once again, they can become home to many of our endangered species.

My four reasons for hope, about which I have written and spoken extensively, are simple—naive perhaps, but they work for me: our quite extraordinary intellect, the resilience of nature, the energy and commitment of informed young people who are empowered to act, and the indomitable human spirit. When human know-how and the resilience of nature are combined with the resourcefulness of dedicated individuals, desecrated landscapes can be given another chance—just as animal and plant species can be saved from extinction.

We have already discussed the restoration of island habitats. Now let me share some of the successful projects that have restored mainland habitats, including streams, rivers, and lakes. Some of these efforts were undertaken with the express intent to save endangered wildlife. In some cases, cleanup efforts were initiated by the government, in others by citizens determined to create a better environment for themselves and their children. A businessman whose operation had caused horrible ecological damage suddenly felt he must put things right; a child made a pledge to restore a mountain—and made his dream come true. All of these efforts are described more fully and illustrated on our Web site.

Kenya Coast: From Wasteland to Paradise

One quite extraordinary project resulted in the transformation of a five-hundred-acre "wasteland," created by twenty years of quarrying by the Bamburi Portland Cement Company, into lush forest and grassland. And the project was initiated—in 1971—not by a group of concerned environmentalists but by Dr. Felix Mandl, the man whose company had caused the devastation. The miraculous change was brought about by the company's remarkable horticulturist, Rene Haller.

When Rene began, the site appeared as "a monstrous lunar-like scar on the landscape, barren, desolate and exposed to the hot tropical sun." The task seemed all but impossible. "It was appalling to note that even in the oldest parts of the quarry no plants had been able to establish themselves," wrote Rene. "I spent countless agonizing hours in the hot and dusty barren land, found a few ferns and perhaps half a dozen tiny bushes and grasses which were struggling to take root, sheltering behind some of the remaining rocks. It was hardly an encouraging environment for tree planting."

Yet today the area is a self-sustaining habitat for wildlife, including thirty species of animals and plants that are on the IUCN endangered species list. And in addition to recreational facilities for visitors, there are countless environmentally sustainable opportunities to improve the lives of the local people. It has become a major environmental education center for Kenya, and is used by schools throughout the country.

From the very beginning of the project, Rene had held the firm belief that, if he looked hard enough, nature would provide the solutions to all his problems. The description of how he tackled his enormous task, step by step, learning from nature, introducing each new species with care, is incredibly interesting and inspirational. It is living proof that the rehabilitation of a man-made wasteland is not only possible, but can be accomplished with sound organic principles.

The Man Who Restored Forests to a Mountain

This story—one of my favorites on our Web site—is about the absurd dream of a six-year-old boy that eventually came true. There was no fairy godmother waving a magic wand—only his sheer determination to make his childish vision into reality.

This hero is Paul Rokich. His father worked for the big copper mine at the foothills of the Oquirrh Mountains in Utah. Paul remembers standing with his father in 1938, when he was six years old, and looking up at the mountains. They were black, the once beautiful forests (that he had seen in a photograph in a school textbook) gone, destroyed by logging, by extensive sheep grazing, and finally by the toxic emissions of the smelting operations.

Paul told his father that one day he would go up those mountains and put the trees back. Surely an impossible task. Yet twenty years later, he set to work to honor his pledge. Every evening, every weekend, year after year, he carried buckets of grass seed up the mountain, driving as far as he could then walking—and sowing. For fifteen years, Paul worked mostly alone, with his own money. Sometimes his family and friends helped. And despite the countless setbacks and disappointments he endured, he never gave up.

Finally the Kennecott Company was shamed into cleaning up the poisonous emissions from its smelting operations, spending millions of dollars. And eventually company managers hired Paul to help them with their belated restoration project. Today the Oquirrh Mountains are green, covered with native grasses and plants originally seeded by Paul, and trees that he planted as seedlings. And the animals have returned.

I have flown over those mountains, looked down on those trees—and marveled. Paul sent me a laminated leaf from one of the very first trees he planted. I carry it around the world, for it symbolizes both the indomitable human spirit and the resilience of nature if given a helping hand.

Sudbury, Ontario

When I first visited Sudbury in the mid-1990s, I heard an extraordinary story that illustrates how a vast landscape utterly devastated by years of destructive human activity can—with time, money, and determination—recover. It is one of the largest community-based environmental restorations of industrially despoiled land ever undertaken. The full story, on our Web site, is amazingly inspirational and one that I never tire of sharing.

It tells how irresponsible logging and industrial pollution gradually created a landscape similar to the surface of the moon, and how the citizens eventually determined to do something about it. I found it so inspiring that I returned, several years later, to learn more. I walked through a glorious landscape where young trees were bursting into spring glory, flowers bloomed everywhere, and the air was full of birdsong. It was almost impossible to believe that, not so long ago, everything had been barren and lifeless—but one area has been left untreated, and the blackened rock is a stark reminder of the harm our species is able to inflict.

The original forests have not returned, nor will they. But the area is beautiful, and much of the wildlife is back. As I turned away from the blackened rocks of yesterday, I was just in time to glimpse the arrow-swift flight of a peregrine falcon—back again after more than fifty years. It was almost as though nature herself was sending me a message of hope to share with the world. They gave me a feather, found near one of the three peregrine nests, as a symbol of all that can be done to heal the scars we have inflicted on Planet Earth.

Before I left Sudbury, I had the joy of releasing a brook trout into the clean water of a stream that had, until recently, been dank, poisoned, lifeless.

Water Is Life

The pollution of our streams, rivers, lakes, and oceans is one of the more shocking results of the use of chemicals and other damaging agents in agriculture, industry, household products, golf courses, and gardens, since much of this poison is washed into the water. Even many of the great aquifers are now polluted. This chemical pollution has led to the destruction of many endangered species' habitats. Yet there are signs of hope here: Slowly our waterways are being cleaned.

I remember when the River Thames in London seemed beyond hope, flowing through London lifeless, contaminated, and murky. Fifty years ago, the Potomac River passed through Washington, DC, stinking like a sewer. And many other major waterways were in much the same state as so many of those in China today. In the United States, Lake Erie was at one time declared a fire hazard, and the Cuyahoga River actually went up in flames and blazed for at least two days! Of course, most species of flora and fauna vanished from such contaminated waters.

Today, however, many of these rivers and lakes have been cleaned up—often at huge expense—and much of the wildlife has returned. A couple of years ago, for example, bass fishing opened up in the Potomac, a clear indication of much cleaner water. Fish are thriving in at least parts of Lake Erie. And fish are back in the River Thames, where waterbirds are once more breeding.

Here I want to mention just a few of the water cleanup projects that have come to my attention, many of which were undertaken in order to protect fish on the endangered species list.

How a Fish Led to the Cleaning of the Hudson River

Thirty years ago, the Hudson River and its surrounding waterways were so polluted that its population of short-nosed sturgeon became the first fish species to be listed (in 1972) as endangered. This resulted in a massive effort to clean up the river. Over the past fifteen years, the population of these fish in the Hudson River (next to one of the busiest cities in the world) has increased by more than 400 percent. The Manhattan area has the most urban estuaries on the planet, so the cleaning of its waters is a major conservation success story. Indeed, the environment has been so improved that there are even plans to introduce oyster reefs and shoreline wetlands in Harlem!

The Amazing Return of the Coho Salmon

In the 1940s, coho were so abundant in California rivers that their numbers were estimated at two to five hundred thousand statewide. And as recently as the 1970s, California's coho fishery still pulled in more than seventy million dollars a year in revenue. But since 1994, commercial fishing for coho has been completely shut down and the fish is listed both state and federally as endangered. It was because of this dramatic decline that a coalition of conservation partners—including landowners and industry—began working to monitor and restore the health of the Garcia watershed, clogged by sediments resulting from irresponsible logging practices.

I happened to be in town when the *San Francisco Chronicle* published an article giving good news. While snorkeling in the headwaters of the Garcia River, Jennifer Carah, a scientist with the Nature Conservancy, and Jonathan Warmerdam from the North Coast Regional Water Quality Control Board, spotted juvenile coho salmon.

I called Jennifer, and she told me that since then young coho had been spotted in five of the twelve sub-watersheds in the river basin. In many of these streams, they had not been seen since the late 1990s. It was an exciting time—Jennifer told me that when she identified those young coho, she "squealed so loudly that Jonathan heard the sound even though we were both underwater"!

There are other great stories, like the demolishing of a lakeside resort to save a minnow-size fish in Nevada, and building an area of wetlands so that carefully selected plants could clean the polluted water of a river in Taiwan. These and other accounts are detailed on our Web site.

Fortunately the looming threat of global water shortage has been acknowledged, and many of the stories in this book describe the efforts of those who are fighting against the reckless use of water for agriculture, industry, and domestic applications, the pollution of rivers and lakes, the draining of the wetlands, and so on.

Today we fight wars about oil, but as Ismail Seregeldin (then with the World Bank) said at the end of the last century: "The wars of the next century will be fought over water." We *could*, with major changes in the way most people live today, survive without oil. But we *could not* survive without water.

Hope for China

Almost always, when I voice my hope that we humans can find a way out of the environmental mess we have made, someone will point out what is happening in China. Do I realize, they want to know, the extent to which that giant country, containing one-fifth of the world's human population, is destroying its environment? And the threat that this poses for the rest of the world? I do, indeed. I have been to China once a year since 1998 and seen with my own eyes the speed of development, the staggering number of new roads and buildings—and cities—that spring up almost overnight. And I know full well that this rapid economic development has taken a heavy toll on the environment. In many cases, it has led to a great deal of human misery also.

As China opened up in the early 1980s, people were offered jobs manufacturing goods for outside markets—and the biggest migration in history was set in motion as the rural poor flocked to the new cities. And there, only too often, they found themselves and their children working in sweatshops, exploited so that China could undercut prices of goods made in the West. They tolerated this because they believed or hoped that it would eventually create a new economy from which they could benefit.

Meanwhile, the level of environmental degradation has soared. Two-thirds of China's main rivers are too polluted for the water to be used for drinking or agriculture. The aquatic ecosystems have been destroyed—the Yangtze River dolphin became extinct. There has been devastating destruction of habitats across the country. And having harmed so much of her own environment, China, desperate to acquire materials such as timber and minerals to sustain her economic growth, is plundering the natural resources of other countries. Especially in Africa where many politicians are willing to sell off the future of their children to make a quick buck.

No wonder so many have given up on China's environment— including many of the Chinese people. But it is important to realize that China is only doing what has been and often still is being done by many other countries. The impact is worse because of the country's staggering number of people and, until fairly recently, the government's refusal to admit there was anything wrong.

The good news is that people in China are now beginning to talk openly about the need to improve the environment and to set aside areas for the conservation of wildlife. (See this book's chapters on the giant panda, the crested ibis, and the milu.) Another story, highlighted on our Web site, describes steps being taken to preserve areas of wetland to benefit the critically endangered Chinese alligator. Moreover, JGI's youth program, Roots & Shoots, which involves young people of all ages in activities to improve the environment for wildlife as well as their own communities, is active in many parts of the country, with offices in Beijing, Shanghai, Chengdu, and Nanchang. There are about six hundred groups in all.

And the story of the Loess Plateau is another reason for hope. It is an area approximately the size of France in the northwest of China. It is home to about ninety million people who were, for many long years, trapped in a vicious cycle of poverty and environmental destruction that only got worse as time went on. For years, the Loess Plateau was considered the most eroded place on earth.

The almost miraculous restoration of this desolate area to a landscape boasting a thriving environment for people and at least some animals has been documented by my friend John Liu in his inspirational film *Earth's Hope*. It illustrates what can be done when a powerful government, backed by the World Bank, decides to take action.

Clearly the hundreds of millions of dollars spent were a wise investment, for already the local communities are thriving. The sense of hopelessness once shared by the population has been replaced by cautious optimism, and young people now expect an education and a future.

And there is hope for wildlife, too. It was decided from the start that there should be clear distinction between land designated for human use, and land that would be most valuable set aside to ensure, for example, protection of the watershed, soil stability, carbon sequestration, and biodiversity. And this "ecological land" could provide a refuge for local endangered species—rescuing them from the extinction many are currently facing.

Lesson from Gombe

The extreme environmental degradation of the Loess Plateau came about because the people sank ever deeper into poverty and hopelessness. Again and again I have seen, as I travel around the developing world, how rural poverty (that so often goes hand in hand with overpopulation) almost invariably causes great damage to the environment. But it was in Tanzania that I suddenly realized that we could only save the Gombe chimpanzees and their forests, in the long term, with the support of the local people. And that we could not hope for such support while they themselves, desperately poor, were struggling to survive.

When, in 1960, I arrived at Gombe National Park to start my chimpanzee study, lush forest stretched for miles along the eastern shores of Lake Tanganyika and inland as far as the eye could see. But over the years, growing populations of local people, swollen by refugees, cut down the trees for firewood and building poles. By the early 1990s, the trees outside the park had almost all gone, and much of the soil was exhausted. Women had to walk farther and farther from their villages in search of fuel wood, adding hours of labor to their already difficult days.

Looking for new land to clear for their crops, people turned to ever steeper and more unsuitable hillsides. With the trees gone, more and more soil was washed away during the rainy season; the soil erosion worsened and landslides became frequent.

By the late 1970s, the chimpanzees were more or less trapped within their tiny thirty-square-mile national park. There could be no exchange of females between groups—which prevents inbreeding—and with only some one hundred individuals remaining, the long-term viability of the Gombe population was grim. Yet how could we even try to protect them while the people outside the park were so desperate, envious of the lush forested area from which they were excluded?

Building Up Goodwill

Clearly it was necessary to gain the goodwill and cooperation of the villagers. In 1994 the Jane Goodall Institute (JGI) initiated TACARE (take care), a program designed to improve the lives of the people in these very poor communities. Project manager George Strunden put together a team of talented and dedicated local Tanzanians who visited the twelve villages closest to Gombe to discuss their problems. They worked out together how TACARE could best help.

Not surprisingly, conservation issues were not listed as top priorities. The main concerns were health, access to clean water, growing more food, and education for their children. And so, working with regional medical authorities, we introduced a new level of primary health care in the villages, including basic information about hygiene and HIV-AIDS. We established tree nurseries and developed ways to restore vitality to exhausted land—farming techniques best suited for the degraded soil. Roots & Shoots, our educational program for youth, was eventually introduced into all the villages. And as TACARE became ever more successful, we were able to start a micro-finance program enabling women to take out very small loans (almost always repaid) to start their own projects—which have to be environmentally friendly and sustainable.

The Importance of Women

All around the world, it has been shown that as women's education improves, family size tends to drop—and after all, it was the growth of the population in the area that first led to the grim conditions TACARE was trying to address. It would be irresponsible to introduce ways of growing more food and saving the lives of more babies, without, at the same time, talking about the need for small families. There are TACARE-trained volunteers from each village, men as well as women, who provide counseling—that is well received—about family planning.

Information about family planning, along with access to health care for her children, enables a woman to realistically plan her family. If she has also received an education, things will go even better. So we started a scholarship program for girls—for a poor family is more likely to educate boys, leaving the girls, once they have finished their first years of compulsory education in the primary schools, to help at home. Some of our girls are now in college.

Restoring and Protecting

Recently I went with our forester, Aristedes Kashula, to one of the villages. A woman demonstrated her new cooking stove, which greatly reduces the amount of firewood she needs. Because all the women get fuel wood from a village woodlot of fast-growing trees, they no longer need to hack at the stumps of trees that once grew on the bare hillside. And such is the regenerative power of nature that a new tree will spring from the seemingly dead stump—and within five years it will be twenty to thirty feet high. Kashula pointed out a hillside now covered in trees. "It's just one of our TACARE forests," he said. "Nine years ago that slope was quite bare."

The villagers gathered under the trees to greet us, including two shy scholarship girls. A ten-year-old R&S leader, confident in his tight-fitting red-striped shirt, told us about the trees his club was planting. I told them how I spoke about the TACARE villages as I traveled around the world. "And," I said, "we must remember to thank the chimps. It was because of them that I came to Tanzania—and see what it has all led to!" I ended with a chimpanzee *pant-hoot* and had all the villagers joining in.

TACARE has greatly improved the lives of the people in twenty-four villages around Gombe, generating a level of cooperation that would have been unthinkable before. And today, under the leadership of Emmanuel Mtiti, we are reaching out to many other villages in the large, mostly degraded area that we call the Greater Gombe ecosystem, with the aim of restoring the forests. Most recently, with government support, we are introducing the TACARE programs in a very large and relatively sparsely populated area to the south, hoping to protect the forests before they are cut down and thus save many of Tanzania's remaining chimpanzees.

Chimpanzees, Corridors, and Coffee

The farmers in the high hills round Gombe grow some of the best coffee in Tanzania, but because of the lack of roads and transport difficulties, they often lump their superior beans with those grown at lower altitudes. Green Mountain Coffee Roasters was the first company to join us in our effort to get these farmers a good price. Now there are a few specialty brands on the market in the United States and Europe, and the farmers—as well as connoisseurs of good coffee—are overjoyed.

The goodwill generated is helping the chimpanzees as well. Every village is required, by the government, to create a Land Management Plan, which includes allocating an agreed percentage of their land for protection or restoration of forest cover. Now many of the villages are setting aside up to 20 percent of their land for forest conservation. They're also working with JGI's amazingly talented Lilian Pintea, an expert in GPS technology and satellite imagery, to ensure that these protected areas will form a corridor so that the chimpanzees will no longer be trapped in the park. That will link them to other remnant populations living in the vast habitats we are helping to protect.

Early in 2009, I stood with Emmanuel Mtiti on a high ridge looking over at the steep hills behind Gombe. A few years ago, those hills had been bare and eroded by desperate attempts to grow crops. Now I could see trees—hundreds and hundreds of them, many more than twelve feet high. This regeneration stretched as far as we could see, toward the Burundi border to the north and the town of Kigoma to the south. It was the first part of the leafy corridor about which I have been dreaming since TACARE started. A last chance for the long-term survival of the Gombe chimpanzees.

Protectors of the World of Plants

For most people, mention of endangered species brings to mind giant pandas, tigers, mountain gorillas, and other such charismatic members of the animal kingdom. Seldom do we think of trees and plants in the same category—as life-forms that, in many cases, we have pushed to the brink of extinction and that desperately need our help if they are to survive.

This discussion about healing earth's scars illustrates that, through a combination of human determination, scientific know-how, and the resilience of nature, even badly compromised habitats can be restored—and time and again we find that it is plants that start the process. Somehow they take root on rock we have laid bare, on land and in water contaminated with pollutants. Slowly they build up the soil and clean the water, paving the way for other life-forms to follow.

Without plants, animals (including ourselves) cannot survive. Herbivores eat plants directly; carnivores eat creatures that have fed on plants—or, to be picky, they may eat animals that fed on animals that fed on plants.

Yet for the most part, the work of the botanists and horticulturalists who battle to save unique plant species from extinction, and to restore habitats, goes unnoticed. The more I thought about this, the more I realized that it was really important to recognize the sometimes extraordinary work that has been and is being done to preserve the rich diversity and sheer beauty of the plant life that brightens our planet. I wanted to acknowledge the contributions of the field botanists who travel to remote places to collect specimens of endangered species, the talented horticulturalists who struggle to germinate reluctant seeds, the skill and patience of those working in herbariums, seed banks, and the many Centers for Plant Conservation that have been established in so many places around the world.

Many of these scientists have generously shared their stories with me or informed me of the work of others. And while unfortunately we cannot pay tribute here to all these champions of the plant kingdom, many of their fascinating stories can be found, gloriously illustrated, on our Web site.

They are dedicated, these custodians of our botanical world. They travel to remote places, searching for rare species, collecting seeds, dangling from ropes to hand-pollinate the last individuals of an endangered plant that has taken refuge in the most inaccessible and inhospitable terrain. They have worked, year after year, to find ways of propagating, in captivity, some plant that is vanishing—or gone from the wild. Some of these heroes I have met, such as Paul Scannell and Andrew Pritchard, who have worked tirelessly for years to protect and restore some of Australia's endangered orchids, and Robert Robichaux, who has devoted his life to saving and restoring the glorious silversword and other Hawaiian plants.

When I visited Kew Botanical Gardens, I heard many fascinating stories about plants in the collection. Carlos Magdalena told me about the café marron, a small flowering shrub that was rediscovered by a schoolboy on Rodrigues Island (off Mauritius) about a hundred years after it was last seen. This was exciting, and the area was searched carefully in the hope that other individuals would be found. It seemed, however, that only the one plant had survived. Carlos described the nightmare of protecting it.

"It was in poor health and attacked by two insect pests," he told me. "It was the last specimen of a species unique in its genus. It did not set seed. There was no information on its cultivation and no other similar surviving species for comparison. Several invasive plant species were growing next to it. It was a few meters off a public road, on a private piece of land, on a remote island with no botanical gardens. And frequently exposed to cyclones!"

Carlos built a cage around the sole survivor shrub to protect it from the locals, who tried to obtain branches for use as a local medicinal remedy. "Somehow somebody managed to jump in and cut the plant almost to ground level . . ."

Eventually, after two years of struggling with bureaucracy, three cuttings from the sickly survivor arrived with Carlos at Kew. And only one grew. Carlos's seventeen-year struggle to persuade the café marron to produce fertile seeds is one of my favorite plant stories.

I asked him how it had felt to be primary caretaker for a very rare specimen like the café marron. "Is is quite a responsibility," he said, "when you suspect or know for certain that if it dies in your glasshouse—the whole species goes. It has scared me to death on several occasions. Going home on a Friday in a summer heat wave and thinking: Will it be there on Monday? . . . Will the person on duty remember to water it properly? Have I watered it too much? Or too little? This is something I'm trying to get used to but I haven't yet!"

I also heard about Cooke's kokio (*Kokia cookei*), a tree discovered in 1860 in Hawaii that was, over the next 118 years, believed on three separate occasions to have become extinct. Each time it was rediscovered years later—only to vanish again. The last time this happened, in 1970, the one remaining tree was killed in a fire. And yet one branch, charred and blackened, was able to provide a few fertile seeds. And so Cooke's kokio lives on.

Carlos showed me a beautiful flowering shrub (*Cylindrocline lorecenci*) that had been—quite literally—raised from the dead. The story illustrates both the resilience of nature and the ingenuity of horticulturists (this time in France). Seeds had been collected fourteen years before the last living plant died, but unfortunately none of them germinated. Still, in just two of those seeds the scientists detected a few live *cells*. And from these, against all odds, they persuaded a new plant to grow.

Finally, on our Web site is the story of a truly dedicated field botanist, Reid Moran. For decades he was a sort of living myth in botanical exploration in Baja California and the Pacific Islands of Mexico. In 1996, Moran wrote *The Flora of Guadalupe Island*, which describes the immense botanical richness of the island but also analyzes, with despair, the devastating impact of the goats and other introduced species. "With its unique flora it is a Mexican treasure that urgently needs protection," he said, "the most beautiful island I know . . ."

Moran retired, but one of his friends, Dr. Exequiel Ezcurra, director of the Biodiversity Research Center of the Californias in San Diego, was a great admirer of Moran's work. A question lingered in Exequiel's mind: Could some of this collapsing paradise, with its incredible biological richness, still be saved? An expedition was organized and it was found that the situation, overall, was bleak, with many of the island's unique species apparently gone and others seeming on the brink of extinction. Unless something was urgently done, the island would be a "paradise lost."

Exequiel told me a dramatic story about the international cooperation and heroic efforts it took to secure funding and painstakingly restore the devastated island to its glorious paradisiacal condition.

In this book, we have shared stories of islands that were restored in order to provide the right habitat for endangered animals. Guadalupe Island was restored primarily to protect its beautiful and endangered flora—although it did see the vitalization of many birds and insects.

This story illustrates, in a striking way, the resilience of nature: Many of the plants on Guadalupe Island had weathered years of a very hostile environment and somehow survived. It is truly a success story, and without the pioneering work of botanist Reid Moran it would never have happened.

Without all the other men and women who are working so hard to conserve and protect our plants and their environments, our planet would be a poorer place. Their efforts are not usually well known, yet their contributions are so important, so meaningful. It is unfortunate that there isn't enough space to pay tribute to them here, but their stories will brighten our Web site and open many eyes to the wonders of the plant kingdom.

Excerpt from *Hope for Animals and Their World*
Why Save Endangered Species?

Jane Goodall, Gail Hudson, and Thane Maynard

Why should we bother to save endangered species? For some, the answer is simple. My friend Shawn Gressel, of the Sioux Tribe in South Dakota, works to reintroduce the swift fox and the black-footed ferret on tribal lands. One day while we sat talking and looking at his photographs, Shawn said to me, "Some people ask me why it matters. They want to know why am I doing it. And I tell them it is because these animals *belong* on the land. They have a right to be there." He feels "obligated" to the animals he is working with.

Shawn is not alone. Many, if not most, of those I have spoken to feel much the same—even if they prefer (or have been advised) to give a scientific explanation of the importance of their work. And of course, there can be no question of the importance of protecting an ecosystem and preventing the loss of biodiversity. Yet there are millions of people who simply "don't get it." Especially if the species concerned is an insect—"Just a bug!" When the Salt Creek tiger beetle was listed as federally endangered, and federal money was released to help safeguard some of the unique and endangered habitat where it lives, there was a heated exchange of e-mails printed in the local Lincoln, Nebraska, newspaper. While many readers welcomed the decision, many others were shocked and horrified; some, too, were genuinely mystified. Here are three examples—and one hears similar opinions in many places.

A man calling himself Dick wrote, "Hundreds of thousands of species have come and gone without humans trying to save them. Even animals we killed off are probably happier now. Look at the dodo bird, what major environmental impact did all of them being wiped out have, other than sailors not having an easy lunch?"

Jill Jenkins asked, "Can someone tell me what difference it would make in our world as a whole, if this beetle were to become extinct?? I am really thankful our U.S. government wasn't around to offer grants to keep the dinosaur from becoming extinct. One half million dollars to save a bug when millions of humans are homeless and hungry. We should be ashamed!"

Then someone named J had this to say: "Now I have heard it all! I am getting so sick of our 'fine' government making kindergarten decisions like this! We need to save our humans that are inflicted with cancer and other life threatening illnesses before we care about this beetle thing! If I saw one in my house I would smash it!"

There were, of course, many letters from people who understood the importance of protecting the environment, even if they did not understand the reasons in detail. Theresa, for example, wrote: "It amazes me how spoiled-rotten Americans are, with our gas-guzzling SUVs and oversized . . . everything! If we don't nurture our habitat, our entire world will become one big Easter Island!" (The full story of the fight to save the Salt Creek tiger beetle can be found on our Web site.)

It is indeed true that the expense of saving an endangered species can be exorbitant, so it is fortunate that in many countries there are laws protecting life-forms threatened with extinction. Else the damage inflicted on the natural world would be even greater. Hundreds of thousands of dollars may be spent on re-routing a road to protect the habitat of some small seemingly insignificant creature; a company may be forced to relocate a proposed development if the area is also home to an endangered species—or else buy suitable land elsewhere and even foot the bill of relocating the species concerned. (There are heartwarming accounts of all this on our Web site.) The reclamation of degraded habitats may cost us dearly, yet these efforts are among the most important facing us as we move into a new millennium.

We Need Wilderness to Nurture Our Souls

Scientists are continually providing facts and figures that can be used to explain the importance, to ourselves and our future, of preserving ecosystems. But the natural world has another value that cannot be expressed in materialistic terms. Twice a year, I spend a few days in Gombe—that's all the time I have. Of course, I hope that I will see the chimpanzees. But I also look forward to the hours I spend alone in the forest, sitting on the peak where I once sat as a young woman and looking out over the forested valleys and the vast expanse of Lake Tanganyika. And I love to sit absorbing the spiritual energy of the Kakombe waterfall as it drops eighty feet to the rocky streambed below, the vegetation constantly moving in the wind of falling water. No wonder the chimpanzees perform their spectacular waterfall displays, "dancing" in the shallow water at the base of the falls, swaying rhythmically from foot to foot, hurling huge rocks, then sitting to watch the mystery of Water—always coming, always going, always there in front of them. No wonder this was one of the sacred places where the medicine men, in the old days, would come to perform their secret rituals. It is these experiences that fill my heart and mind with peace—being, even for a short time, part of the forest, connected once more with the mystery, feeding my soul.

Jeremy Madeiros, who has dedicated his life's work to protecting the Bermuda petrels, or cahow, told me how he was taken to a California redwood forest when he was eleven years old. For him, being among those giant ancient trees was a spiritual experience, as it is for so many of us. "It was a defining moment in my life," he told me. "It determined my future path."

Rod Sayler, working to save the pygmy rabbit in Washington State, believes that human values and ethics should, where possible, drive the saving of endangered species. "We are treading too harshly on the earth and consuming and degrading too much of the planet," he said. "If we allow extinctions to happen through ignorance or greed, then with the loss of each endangered species and unique population, our world becomes less diverse and strikingly less beautiful and mysterious. Our oceans, grasslands, and forests will echo with silence, and the human heart will know that something is missing—but it will be too late." He argues that, although the fight to save endangered species may be costly, "can the human spirit afford not to try? If we do not, someday we will look back with the wisdom of time and regret our decision."

The Keepers of the Planet: What Keeps Them Going

Fortunately for the future of the planet and all its life-forms, including us and our children, there are, as we have seen, brave souls out there fighting day after day to save what is left and restore what has gone. Working on this book has been a real privilege, for I have met so many of these extraordinary, dedicated, and passionate people from around the globe. Many of them, as described, have spent years working in remote places, enduring considerable personal discomfort and sometimes very real dangers. They have had to battle, too, not only with the harsher aspects of nature but also with uninformed, unimaginative, and shortsighted officials who refuse permission to move ahead with urgently needed management actions. Yet they have not given up.

What keeps them going? I asked some of those who have been longest in the field. All of them confessed to loving the wilderness, being out there with nature. And, as well, they became utterly absorbed in the work—almost, for some of them, it was like a mission. They simply couldn't give up. They became, as the wife of Dean Biggins (one of the black-footed ferret team) put it, "obsessed."

Don Merton, who has worked so hard to protect island birds, told me that most of all he loved "the ultimate challenge—fighting to save the last few individuals of a unique life-form. The black robin is one of New Zealand's living treasures . . . I felt a massive responsibility to current and future generations to save this fantastic little bird from the brink of extinction." He told me that he could hardly wait to get back to the field each spring to find out how the individual birds had fared. And, he said, "Some of my colleagues became annoyed with me when I rose very early to start searching at first light, and woke them!"

Chris Lucash, after twenty-one years with the Red Wolf Recovery Program, told me that during the early years when they were releasing the wolves into the wild, he felt privileged to have the opportunity of being part of something he believed was so very important. "I had unwavering energy," he said. "I had a difficult time sleeping and wanted only to stay out keeping track of the wolves and try to figure out everywhere they went, what they did, why they did it, what they ate. I took little or no time off. I lived red wolves, and was baffled, confused by, and almost intolerant of people—friends and family—who did not feel the way I did about the program." And still, after more than twenty years working with the wolves, he looks forward to going to work "every day—sometimes even on Sundays!"

Daring to Admit That We Love

There is another aspect of their work that for some may be the most important—the relationship they establish with the animals they work with. I have described my own feelings for so many of Gombe's chimpanzees. The one I loved best was David Greybeard, the first who lost his fear of me, who allowed me to groom him and tolerated my following him in the forest. And I remember, as though it happened but yesterday, the day I offered him a palm nut on my outstretched hand. Not wanting it, he turned away, but then he turned back and, looking directly into my eyes, took the nut, dropped it, then very gently squeezed my hand with his fingers. A chimpanzee gesture of reassurance. And so we communicated perfectly, he and I, with shared gestures that, surely, predate our human spoken language.

Unfortunately in our materialistic world, where all that counts is the bottom line, human values of love and compassion are too often suppressed. To admit you care about animals, that you feel passionately about them, that you love them, is sometimes counterproductive for those in conservation work and science. Emotional involvement with one's subject is considered inappropriate by many scientists; scientific observations should be objective. Anyone who admits to truly caring about, having empathy with, an animal is liable to be written off as sentimental, and their research will be suspect.

Fortunately, most of the extraordinary individuals whose work is discussed in this book are not afraid of showing that they care. (Particularly those who have retired!) During one of my discussions with Carl Jones, of Mauritius Island fame, he echoed my own belief—that although scientists must have the ability to stand back and observe objectively, "they should also have empathy." Humans, he said, "are intuitive and empathetic before they are coldly scientific"—and he believes that most "scientists call on these underlying qualities every day." When he was working to save the Mauritius kestrels, he got to know and understand each bird as an individual. Don Merton waxed lyrical over the black robins, "those delightful, tame, friendly little birds." Over the years, Don said, "I naturally became very attached— even emotionally involved you might say! I just loved them." And Len Zeoli, when I asked him what motivated him to keep on working to save the pygmy rabbits, said simply, "How can you see one, know one, and not love these little creatures? That's what drives us. That is what keeps us going."

Mike Pandey, while filming in India the barbaric method of killing gentle, harmless whale sharks, came across a huge individual who was dying. "It slowly turned to look at me . . . beseeching and pleading . . . the intelligent eyes spoke a million words." He said he would never forget that look: "Suddenly I was in communication with the majestic creature and there was a deep-rooted bonding." That was the turning point that transformed his life. He decided to "speak out for the voiceless" and started his long series of powerful films for conservation.

Brent Houston told me of the time when a young black-footed ferret approached him as he sat near the den, in the first light of day. "Without warning, he approached my foot and sniffed my hiking boot . . . I thought the pounding of my heart would scare him, but I remained still, desperate for some sort of connection. He looked right up at me and at my face, into my eyes. And then the most extraordinary thing happened. This young ferret, looking up at me with his big round eyes, put his little black foot on my hiking boot and he held it there. I looked right at him and he looked at me and he saw me smile. It was one of the most satisfying moments in my long career of observing wildlife. Here was one of the last black-footed ferrets in the world reaching out to me, trusting me, perhaps even asking for my help."

It is this—this link between the human being and the other animals with whom we share Planet Earth, this connection we can establish with another life-form—that for many makes it possible to carry on. To carry on with work that can be so hard, carry on despite the frustrations and setbacks, and sometimes the outright hostility or ridicule of those who believe that to save any species from extinction is sentimental and a waste of money and resources.

But they cannot do it alone, these Keepers of the Planet. To save Planet Earth, each of us who cares must become involved in protecting and restoring the wild places and the animals and plants that live there. We hope that this book, together with our Web site, overflowing with stories of passionate, dedicated, and always hopeful people, whose efforts have saved myriad life-forms from extinction, will encourage those who are out there now, working tirelessly as they try to save other highly endangered animals and plants, each one precious and unique. And those who are striving to prevent further species from becoming endangered. And yet others fighting to restore and protect the environment. Their tasks sometimes seem almost impossible—and if they had no hope of success, they would surely give up.

If we are without hope we fall into apathy. Without hope nothing will change. That is why we feel it is so desperately important to share our own, irrepressible hope for the animals and their world.

Excerpt from *Earth in Mind: On Education, Environment, and the Human Prospect*

Love It or Lose It: The Coming Biophilia Revolution

David W. Orr

I have set before you life and death, blessing and cursing:
therefore choose life, that both thou and thy seed may live.
—Deutronomy 30:19

"Nature and I are two," filmmaker Woody Allen once said, and apparently the two have not gotten together yet (Lax, 1992, pp. 39–40). Allen is known to take extraordinary precautions to limit bodily and mental contact with rural flora and fauna. He does not go in natural lakes, for example, because "there are live things in there." The nature Allen does find comfortable is that of New York City, a modest enough standard for wildness.

Allen's aversion to nature, what can be called biophobia, is increasingly common among people raised with television, Walkman radios attached to their heads, and video games and living amidst shopping malls, freeways, and dense urban or suburban settings where nature is permitted tastefully, as decoration. More than ever we dwell in and among our own creations and are increasingly uncomfortable with nature lying beyond our direct control. Biophobia ranges from discomfort in "natural" places to active scorn for whatever is not manmade, managed, or air-conditioned. Biophobia, in short, is the culturally acquired urge to affiliate with technology, human artifacts, and solely with human interests regarding the natural world. I intend the word broadly to include as well those who regard nature "objectively" as nothing more than "resources" to be used any way the favored among the present generation see fit.

Is biophobia a problem as, say, misanthropy or sociopathy, or is it merely a personal preference; one plausible view of nature among many? Is it OK that Woody Allen feels little or no sympathy or kinship with nature? Does it matter that a growing number of other people do not like it or like it only in the abstract as nothing more than resources to be managed or as television nature specials? Does it matter that we are increasingly separated from the conditions of nature? If these things do matter, how do they matter and why? And why have so many come to think that the created world is inadequate? Inadequate to what and for what?

At the other end of the continuum of possible orientation toward nature is "biophilia," which E. O. Wilson (1984) has defined as "the urge to affiliate with other forms of life" (p. 85). Erich Fromm (1973) once defined it more broadly as "the passionate love of life and of all that is alive" (pp. 365–366). Both agree, however, that biophilia is innate and a sign of mental and physical health. To what extent are our biological prospects and our sanity now dependent on our capacity for biophilia? To that degree it is important that we understand how biophilia comes to be, how it prospers, what competencies and abilities it requires of us, and how these are to be learned.

Biophilia is not all that tugs at us. The affinity for life or biophilia competes with other drives and affinities, including biophobia disguised beneath the abstractions and presumptions of progress found in economics, management, and technology. Whatever is in our genes, then, the affinity for life is now a choice we must make. Compared with earlier cultures, our distinction lies in the fact that technology now allows us to move much further toward total domination of nature than ever before. Serious and well-funded people talk about reweaving the fabric of life on earth through genetic engineering and nanotechnologies, others talk of leaving the earth altogether for space colonies, and still others talk of reshaping human consciousness to fit "virtual reality." If we are to preserve a world in which biophilia can be expressed and can flourish, we will have to decide to make such a world.

The Origins and Consequences of Biophobia

In varying degrees humans have always modified their environments. I am persuaded that they generally have intended to do so with decorum and courtesy toward nature—not always and everywhere to be sure, but mostly. On balance, the evidence further suggests that biophilia or something close to it was woven throughout the myths, religions, and mindset of early humankind, which saw itself as participating with nature. In Owen Barfield's words, people once felt "integrated or mortised into" the world in ways that we do not and perhaps cannot (Barfield, 1957, p. 78). Technology, primitive by our standards, set limits on what tribal cultures could do to the world, while their myths, superstitions, and taboos constrained what they thought they ought to do. But I do not think that early humans *chose* biophilia, if for no other reason than that there was no choice to be made. And those tribes and cultures that were biophobic or incompetent toward nature passed into oblivion through starvation and disease (Diamond, 1992, pp. 317–338).

Looking back across that divide, I think it is evident that tribal cultures possessed an ecological innocence of sorts because they did not have the possibilities or the knowledge given to us. We, in contrast, must choose between biophobia and biophilia because science and technology have given us the power to destroy so completely as well as the knowledge to understand the consequences of doing so. The divide was not a sharp break but a kind of slow tectonic shift in perception and attitudes that widened throughout the late Middle Ages to the present. What we call "modernization" represented dramatic changes in how we regard the natural world and our role in it. These changes are now so thoroughly ingrained in us that we can scarcely conceive of any other manner of thinking. But crossing this divide first required us to discard the belief that the world was alive and worthy of respect, if not fear. To dead matter, we owe no obligations. Second, it was necessary to distance ourselves from animals who were transformed by Cartesian alchemy into mere machines. Again, no obligations or pity are owed to machines. In both cases, use is limited only by usefulness. Third, it was necessary to quiet whatever remaining sympathy we had for nature in favor of "hard" data that could be weighed, measured, counted, and counted on to make a profit. Fourth, we needed a reason to join power, cash, and knowledge in order to transform the world into more useful forms. Francis Bacon provided the logic, and the evolution of government-funded research did the rest. Fifth, we required a philosophy of improvement and found it in the ideology of perpetual economic growth, now the central mission of governments everywhere. Sixth, biophobia required the sophisticated cultivation of dissatisfaction, which could be converted into mass consumption. The advertising industry and the annual style change were invented.

For these revolutions to work, it was necessary that nature be rendered into abstractions and production statistics of board feet, tons, barrels, and yield. It was also necessary to undermine community, especially the small community, where attachment to place might grow and with it resistance to crossing the divide. Finally it was necessary to convert politics into the pursuit of material self-interest and hence render people impotent as citizens and unable to talk of larger and more important things.

To this point the story is well known, but it is hardly finished. Genetic engineers are busy remaking the fabric of life on earth. The development of nanotechnologies—machines at the molecular level—create possibilities for good and evil that defy prediction. How long will it be until the genetic engineers or nanotechnologists release an AIDS-like virus? One can only guess. But even those promoting such technologies admit that they "carry us toward unprecedented dangers . . . more potent than nuclear weapons" (Drexier, 1987, p. 174). And immediately ahead is the transformation of human consciousness brought on by the conjunction of neuroscience and computers in machines that will simulate whatever reality we choose. What happens to the quality of human experience or to our politics when cheap and thoroughgoing fantasy governs our mental life? In each case, untransformed nature pales by comparison. It is clumsy, inconvenient, flawed, and difficult to move or rearrange. It is slow. And it cannot be converted to mass dependence and profits so easily.

Beneath each of these endeavors lies a barely concealed contempt for unaltered life and nature, as well as contempt for the people who are expected to endure the mistakes, purchase the results, and live with the consequences, whatever those may be. It is a contempt disguised by terms of bamboozlement, like *bottom line*, *progress*, *needs*, *costs and benefits*, *economic growth*, *jobs*, *realism*, *research*, and *knowledge*, words that go undefined and unexamined. Few people, I suspect, believe "in their bones" that the net results from all of this will be positive, but most feel powerless to stop what seems to be so inevitable and unable to speak what is so hard to say in the language of self-interest.

The manifestation of biophobia, explicit in the urge to control nature, has led to a world in which it is becoming easier to be biophobic. Undefiled nature is being replaced by a defiled nature of landfills, junkyards, strip mines, clear-cuts, blighted cities, six-lane freeways, suburban sprawl, polluted rivers, and superfund sites, all of which deserve our phobias. Ozone depletion, meaning more eye cataracts and skin cancer, does give more reason to stay indoors. The spread of toxic substances and radioactivity does mean more disease. The disruption of natural cycles and the introduction of exotic species has destroyed much of the natural diversity that formerly graced our landscapes. Introduced blights and pests have or are destroying

American chestnuts, elms, maples, dogwoods, hemlocks, and ashes. Global warming will degrade the flora and fauna of familiar places (Peters and Myers, 1991–1992, pp. 66–72). Biophobia sets into motion a vicious cycle that tends to cause people to act in such a way as to undermine the integrity, beauty, and harmony of nature, creating the very conditions that make the dislike of nature yet more probable.

Even so, is it OK that Woody Allen, or anyone else, does not like nature? Is biophobia merely one among a number of equally legitimate ways to relate to nature? I do not think so. First, for every "biophobe" others have to do that much more of the work of preserving, caring for, and loving the nature that supports biophobes and biophiliacs alike. Economists call this the "free-rider problem." It arises in every group, committee, or alliance when it is possible for some to receive all of the advantages of membership while doing none of the work necessary to create those advantages. Environmental free riders benefit from others' willingness to fight for the clean air that they breathe, the clean water that they drink, the preservation of biological diversity that sustains them, and the conservation of the soil that feeds them. But they lift not a finger. Biophobia is not OK because it does not distribute fairly the work of keeping the earth or any local place.

Biophobia is not OK for the same reason that misanthropy and sociopathy are not OK. We recognize these as the result of deformed childhoods that create unloving and often violent adults. Biophobia in all of its forms similarly shrinks the range of experiences and joys in life in the same way that the inability to achieve close and loving relationships limits a human life. E. O. Wilson (1984) put it this way:

> People can grow up with the outward appearance of normality in an environment largely stripped of plants and animals, in the same way that passable looking monkeys can be raised in laboratory cages and cattle fattened in feeding bins. Asked if they were happy, these people would probably say yes. Yet something vitally important would be missing, not merely the knowledge

> and pleasure that can be imagined and might have been, but a
> wide array of experiences that the human brain is peculiarly
> equipped to receive. (p. 118)

Can the same be said of whole societies that distance themselves from animals, trees, landscapes, mountains, and rivers? Is mass biophobia a kind of collective madness? In time I think we will come to know that it is.

Biophobia is not OK because it is the foundation for a politics of domination and exploitation. For our politics to work as they now do, a large number of people must not like any nature that cannot be repackaged and sold back to them. They must be ecologically illiterate and ecologically incompetent, and they must believe that this is not only inevitable but desirable. Furthermore, they must be ignorant of the basis of their dependency. They must come to see their bondage as freedom and their discontents as commercially solvable problems. The drift toward a biophobic society, as George Orwell and C. S. Lewis foresaw decades ago, requires the replacement of nature and human nature by technology and the replacement of real democracy by a technological tyranny now looming on the horizon.

These are reasons of self-interest: It is to our advantage to distribute the world's work fairly, to build a society in which lives can be lived fully, and to create an economy in which people participate knowledgeably. There is a further argument against biophobia that rests not on our self-interest, but on our duties. Finally, biophobia is not OK because it violates an ancient charge to replenish the earth. In return for our proper use, the earth is given to humankind as a trust. Proper use requires gratitude, humility, charity, and skill. Improper use begins with ingratitude and disparagement and proceeds to greed, abuse, and violence. We cannot forsake the duties of stewardship without breaking another trust with those who preceded us and with those who will follow.

Biophobia is certainly more complex than I have described it. One can be both biophobic and a dues-paying member of the Sierra Club.

It is possible to be nature averse but still "like" the idea of nature as an abstraction. Moreover, it is possible to adopt the language and guise of biophilia and do a great deal of harm to the earth, knowingly or unknowingly. In other words, it is possible for us to be inconsistent, hypocritical, and ignorant of what we do.

But is it possible for us to be neutral or "objective" toward life and nature? I do not think so. On closer examination, what often passes for neutrality is nothing of the sort but rather the thinly disguised self-interest of those with much to gain financially or professionally. For those presuming to wear the robes of objectivity, the guise, in Abraham Maslow's (1966) words, is often "a defense against being flooded by the emotions of humility, reverence, mystery, wonder and awe" (p. 139). Life ought to excite our passion, not our indifference. Life in jeopardy ought to cause us to take a stand, not retreat into a spurious neutrality. Furthermore, it is a mistake to assume that commitment precludes the ability to think clearly and to use evidence accurately. To the contrary, commitment motivates intellectual clarity, integrity, and depth. We understand this in other realms quite well. When the chips are down, we do not go to physicians who admit to being neutral about the life and death of their patients. Nor when our hide is at stake do we go to lawyers who profess "objective" neutrality between justice and injustice. It is a mistake to think that matters of environment and life on earth are somehow different. They are not, and we cannot in such things remain aloof or indifferent without opening the world to demons.

Biophilia

We relate to the environment around us in different ways, with differing intensity, and these bonds have different sources. At the most common level, we learn to love what has become familiar. There are prisoners who prefer their jail cell to freedom; city dwellers, like Woody Allen, who shun rural landscapes or wilderness; and rural folk who will not set foot in the city. Simply put, we tend to bond with what we know well. Geographer Yi-Fu Tuan (1974) described this bonding as "topophilia," which includes "all of the human being's affective ties with the material environment" (p. 93). Topophilia is rooted less in our deep psychology than it is in our particular circumstances and experiences. It is closer to a sense of habitat that is formed out of the familiar circumstances of everyday living than it is a genuine rootedness in the biology and topography of a particular place. It is not innate, but acquired. New Yorkers have perhaps a greater sense of topophilia or habitat than do residents of Montana. But Montanans are more likely to feel kinship with sky, mountains, and trout streams. Both, however, tend to be comfortable with what has become habitual and familiar.

E. O. Wilson (1984) suggested a deeper source of attachment that goes beyond the particularities of habitat. "We are," he argues, "a biological species [that] will find little ultimate meaning apart from the remainder of life" (p. 112). We are bound to living things by what Wilson described as an innate urge to affiliate, or "biophilia," which begins in early childhood and "cascades" into cultural and social patterns. Biophiha is inscribed in the brain itself, expressing tens of thousands of years of evolutionary experience. It is evident in our preference for landscapes that replicate the savannas on which mind evolved: "Given a completely free choice, people gravitate statistically toward a savanna-like environment" (Wilson, 1984, p. 115). Removed to purely artificial environments and deprived of "beauty and mystery," the mind "will drift to simpler and cruder configurations," which undermine sanity itself (Wilson, 1984, p. 118). Still, biophilia competes with what Wilson describes as the "audaciously destructive tendencies of our species" that seem also to have "archaic biological origins" (p. 121). Allowing these tendencies free rein to destroy the world "in which the brain was assembled over millions of years" is, Wilson has argued, "a risky step."

A third possibility is that at some level of alertness and maturity, we respond with awe to the natural world independent of any instinctual conditioning. "If you study life deeply," Albert Schweitzer (1969) once wrote, "its profundity will seize you suddenly with dizziness" (p. 115).

He described this response as "reverence for life" arising from the awareness of the unfathomable mystery of life itself. (The German word Schweitzer used, *Ehrfurcht*, implies greater awe than is implied by the English word *reverence*.) Reverence for life, I think, is akin to what Rachel Carson (1965/1987) meant by "the sense of wonder." But for Schweitzer (1972) reverence for life originated in large measure from the intellectual contemplation of the world: "Let a man once begin to think about the mystery of his life and the links which connect him with the life that fills the world, and he cannot but bring to bear upon his own life and all other life that comes within his reach the principle of Reverence for Life" (p. 231). Schweitzer regarded reverence for life as the only possible basis for a philosophy on which civilization might be restored from the decay he saw throughout the modern world. "We must," he wrote, "strive together to attain to a theory of the universe affirmative of the world and of life" (Schweitzer, 1972, p. 64).

We have reason to believe that this intellectual striving is aided by what is already innate in us and may be evident in other creatures. No less an authority than Charles Darwin believed that "all animals feel wonder" (Darwin, 1977, p. 450). Primatologist Harold Bauer once observed a chimpanzee lost in contemplation by a spectacular waterfall in the Gombe Forest Reserve in Tanzania. Contemplation finally gave way to "pant-hoot" calls while the chimp ran back and forth drumming on trees with its fists (Konner, 1982, p. 431). No one can say for certain what this behavior means, but it is not farfetched to see it as a chimpanzee version of awe and ecstasy. Jane Goodall and others have described similar behavior. It would be the worst kind of anthropocentrism to dismiss such accounts in the belief that the capacity for biophilia and awe is a human monopoly. In fact it may be that we have to work at it harder than other creatures. Joseph Wood Krutch (1991), for one, believed that for birds and other creatures "joy seems to be more important and more accessible than it is to us" (p. 227). And not a few philosophers have agreed with Abraham Heschel (1990) that "as civilization advances, the sense of wonder almost necessarily declines" (p. 37).

Do we, with all of our technology, retain a built-in affinity for nature? I think so, but I know of no proof that would satisfy skeptics. If we do have such an innate sense, we might nevertheless conclude from the damage that we have done to the world that biophilia does not operate everywhere and at all times. It may be, as Erich Fromm (1973) argued, that biophilia can be dammed up or corrupted and can subsequently appear in other, more destructive forms:

> Destructiveness is not parallel to, but the alternative to biophilia. Love of life or love of the dead is the fundamental alternative that confronts every human being. Necrophilia grows as the development of biophilia is stunted. Man is biologically endowed with the capacity for biophilia, but psychologically he has the potential for necrophilia as an alternative solution. (p. 366)

We also have reason to believe that people can lose the sense of biophilia. For example, in his autobiography, Darwin (1958) admitted that "fine scenery . . . does not cause me the exquisite delight which it formerly did" (p. 54). It is also possible that entire societies can lose the capacity for love of any kind. When the Ik tribe in northern Uganda was forcibly moved from its traditional hunting grounds into a tiny reserve, their world, as Colin Turnbull (1972) expressed it, "became something cruel and hostile," and they "lost whatever love they might once have had for their mountain world" (pp. 256, 259). The love for their place the Ik people may have once felt was transmuted into boredom and a "moody distrust" of the world around them and matched by social relations that Turnbuhl described as utterly loveless, cruel, and despicable. The Ik are a stark warning to us that the ties to life and to each other are more fragile than some suppose and, once broken, are not easily repaired or perhaps cannot be repaired at all.

Much of the history of the twentieth century offers further evidence of the fragility of biophilia and of philia. Ours is a time of unparalleled human violence and unparalleled violence toward nature. This is the century of Auschwitz and the mass extinction of species, nuclear weapons, and exploding economic growth.

Even if we could find no evidence of a lingering human affinity or affection for nature, however, humankind is now in the paradoxical position of having to learn altruism and selflessness, but for reasons of survival that are reasons of self-interest. In the words of Stephen Jay Gould (1991), "We cannot win this battle to save species and environments without forging an emotional bond between ourselves and nature as well—for we will not fight to save what we do not love" (p. 14). And if we do not save species and environments, we cannot save ourselves; we depend on those species and environments in more ways than we can possibly know. We have, in other words, "purely rational reasons" to cultivate biophilia (Wilson, 1984, p. 140).

Beyond our physical survival, there is still more at risk. The same Faustian urges that drive the ecological crisis also erode those qualities of heart and mind that constitute the essence of our humanity. Bertrand Russell (1959) put it this way:

> It is only in so far as we renounce the world as its lovers that we can conquer it as its technicians. But this division in the soul is fatal to what is best in man. . . . The power conferred by science as a technique is only obtainable by something analogous to the worship of Satan, that is to say, by the renunciation of love. . . . The scientific society in its pure form . . . is incompatible with the pursuit of truth, with love, with art, with spontaneous delight, with every ideal that men have hitherto cherished. (p. 264)

The ecological crisis, in short, is about what it means to be human. And if natural diversity is the wellspring of human intelligence, then the systematic destruction of nature inherent in contemporary technology and economics is a war against the very sources of mind. We have good reason to believe that human intelligence could not have evolved in a lunar landscape, devoid of biological diversity. We also have good reason to believe that the sense of awe toward the creation had a great deal to do with the origin of language and that early hominids *wanted* to talk, sing, and write poetry in the first place. Elemental things like flowing water, wind, trees, clouds, rain, mist, mountains, landscape, animals, changing seasons, the night sky, and the mysteries of the life cycle gave birth to thought and language. They continue to do so, but perhaps less exuberantly than they once did. For this reason I think it not possible to unravel natural diversity without undermining human intelligence as well. Can we save the world and anything like a human self from the violence we have unleashed without biophilia and reverence for the creation? All the arguments made by technological fundamentalists and by the zealots of instrumental rationality notwithstanding, I know of no good evidence that we can. We must choose, in Joseph Wood Krutch's (1991) words, whether "we want a civilization that will move toward some more intimate relation with the natural world or . . . one that will continue to detach and isolate itself from both a dependence upon and a sympathy with that community of which we were originally a part?" (p. 165). The writer of Deuteronomy had it right. Whatever our feelings, however ingenious our philosophies, whatever innate gravity tugs at us, we must finally choose between life and death, between intimacy and isolation.

Biophilia: Eros to Agape

We are now engaged in a great global debate about what it means to live "sustainably" on the earth. This word, however, is fraught with confusion, in large part because we are trying to define it before we have decided whether we want an intimate relation with nature or total mastery, as Krutch (1991) put it. We cannot know what sustainability means until we have decided what we intend to sustain and how we propose to do so. For some, sustainability means maintaining our present path of domination, only with greater efficiency. But were we to decide, in concurrence with Krutch and others, that we do want an intimate relation with nature, to take nature as our standard, what does that mean? We must choose along the continuum that runs between biophilia and biophobia and between intimacy and mastery, but how can we know when we have crossed over from one to the other? The choices are not always so simple, nor will they be presented to us so candidly.

The options, even the most destructive, will be framed as life-serving, as necessary for a greater good someday, or as simply inevitable since "you can't stop progress." How, then, can we distinguish those things that serve life broadly and well from those that diminish it?

Biophilia is a kind of philia or love, but what kind? The Greeks distinguished three kinds of love: *eros*, meaning love of beauty or romantic love aiming to possess; *agape*, or sacrificial love, which asks nothing in return; and *philia*, or the love between friends. The first two of these reveal important parts of biophilia, which probably begins as eros but matures, if at all, as a form of agape. For the Greeks eros went beyond sensuous love to include creature needs for food, warmth, and shelter, as well as higher needs to understand, appreciate, and commune with nature (Bratton, 1992, p. 11). But eros aims no higher than self-fulfillment. Defined as an "innate urge," biophilia is eros, reflecting human desire and self-interest, including the interest in survival.

Biophilia as eros, however, traps us in a paradox. According to Susan Bratton (1992), "Without agape, human love for nature will always be dominated by unrestrained eros and distorted by extreme self-interest and material valuation" (p. 15). What we love only from self-interest, we will sooner or later destroy. Agape tempers our use of nature so that "God's providence is respectfully received and insatiable desire doesn't attempt to extract more from creation than it can sustain" (Bratton, 1992, p. 13). Agape enlarges eros, bringing humans and the creation together so that it is not possible to love either humanity or nature without also loving and serving the other. Agape in this sense is close to Schweitzer's description of "reverence for life," which calls us to transcend even the most enlightened calculations of self-interest. Wouldn't respect for nature do as well? I think not, and for the reason that it is just too bloodless, too cool, and too self-satisfied and aloof to cause us to do much to save species and environments. I am inclined to agree with Stephen Jay Gould that we will have to reach deeper.

What, then, do we know about deeper sources of motivation, including the ways in which eros is transformed into agape, and what does this reveal about biophilia? First, we know that the capacity for love of any kind begins early in the life and imagination of the child. The potential for biophilia possibly begins at birth, as Robert Coles once surmised, with the newborn infant being introduced to its place in nature (Coles, 1971). If so, the manner and circumstances of birth are more important than is usually thought. Biophilia is certainly evident in the small child's efforts to establish intimacy with the earth, like that of Jane Goodall, age two, sleeping with earthworms under her pillow (Montgomery, 1991, p. 28), or John Muir (1988), "reveling in the wonderful wildness" around his boyhood Wisconsin home (p. 43). If by some fairly young age, however, nature has not been experienced as a friendly place of adventure and excitement, biophilia will not take hold as it might have. An opportunity will have passed, and thereafter the mind will lack some critical dimension of perception and imagination.

Second, I think we know that biophilia requires easily and safely accessible places where it might take root and grow. For Aldo Leopold it began in the marshes and woods along the Mississippi River. For young E. O. ("Snake") Wilson (1984) it began in boyhood explorations of the "woods and swamps in a languorous mood . . . [forming] the habit of quietude and concentration" (pp. 86–92). The loss of places such as these is one of the uncounted costs of economic growth and urban sprawl. It is also a powerful argument for containing that sprawl and expanding urban parks and recreation areas.

Third, I think we can safely surmise that biophilia, like the capacity to love, needs the help and active participation of parents, grandparents, teachers, and other caring adults. Rachel Carson's (1987) relation with her young nephew caused her to conclude that the development of a child's sense of wonder required "the companionship of at least one adult who can share it, rediscovering with him the joy, excitement and mystery of the world we live in" (p. 45). For children the sense of biophilia needs instruction, example, and validation by a caring adult. And for adults, rekindling the sense of wonder may require a child's excitement and openness to natural wonders as well.

Fourth, we have every reason to believe that love and biophilia alike flourish mostly in good communitites. I do not mean necessarily affluent places. In fact, affluence often works against real community, as surely as does violence and utter poverty. By community I mean, rather, places in which the bonds between people and those between people and the natural world create a pattern of connectedness, responsibility, and mutual need. Real communities foster dignity, competence, participation, and opportunities for good work. And good communities provide places in which children's imagination and earthy sensibilities root and grow.

Fifth, we have it on good authority that love is patient, kind, enduring, hopeful, long-suffering, and truthful, not envious, boastful, insistent, arrogant, rude, self-centered, irritable, and resentful (I Corinthians 13). For biophilia to work, I think it must have similar qualities. Theologian James Nash (1991) for example proposed six ecological dimensions of love: (1) beneficence, e.g., kindness to wild creatures; (2) other-esteem, which rejects the idea of possessing or managing the biosphere; (3) receptivity to nature, e.g., awe; (4) humility, by which is meant caution in the use of technology; (5) knowledge of ecology and how nature works; and (6) communion as "reconciliation, harmony, koinonia, shalom" between humankind and nature (pp. 139–161). I would add only that real love does not do desperate things, and it does not commit the irrevocable.

Sixth, I think we know with certainty that beyond some scale and level of complexity, the possibility for love of any sort declines. Beneficence, awe, reconciliation, and communion are not entirely probable attitudes for the poverty stricken living in overcrowded barrios. With 10 or 12 billion people on the earth, we will have no choice but to try to manage nature, even though it will be done badly. The desperate and the hungry will not be particularly cautious with risky technologies. Nor will the wealthy, fed and supplied by vast, complex global networks, understand the damage they cause in distant places they never see and the harm they do to people they will never know. Knowledge has its own limits of scale.

Beyond some level of scale and complexity, the effects of technology, used in a world we cannot fully comprehend, are simply unknowable. When the genetic engineers and the nanotechnologists finally cause damage to the earth comparable to that done by the chemists who invented and so casually and carelessly deployed chlorofluorocarbons, they too will plead for forgiveness on the grounds that they did not know what they were doing.

Seventh, love, as Eric Fromm (1989) wrote, is an art, the practice of which requires "discipline, concentration and patience throughout every phase of life" (p. 100). The art of biophilia, similarly, requires us to use the world with disciplined, concentrated, and patient competence. To live and earn our livelihood means that we must "daily break the body and shed the blood of creation," in Wendell Berry's (1981) words. Our choice is whether we do so "knowingly, lovingly, skillfully, reverently . . . [or] ignorantly, greedily, clumsily, destructively" (p. 281). Practice of any art also requires forbearance, which means the ability to say no to things that diminish the object of love or our capacity to work artfully. And for the same reasons that it limits the exploitation of persons, forbearance sets limits on our use of nature.

Finally, we know that for love to grow from eros to agape, something like *metanoia*, or the "transformation of one's whole being" is necessary. Metanoia is more than a "paradigm change." It is a change, first, in our loyalties, affections, and basic character, which subsequently changes our intellectual priorities and paradigms. For whole societies, the emergence of biophilia as agape will require something like a metanoia that deepens our loyalty and affections to life and over time alters the character of our entire civilization.

The Biophilia Revolution

"Is it possible," E. O. Wilson (1984) asked, "that humanity will love life enough to save it?" (p. 145). And if we do love life enough to save it, what is required of us? On one level the answer is obvious. We need to transform how and how rapidly we use the earth's endowment of land, minerals, water, air, wildlife, and fuels: an efficiency revolution that buys us some time. Beyond efficiency, we need another revolution that transforms our ideas of what it means to live decently and how little is actually necessary for a decent life: a sufficiency revolution. The first revolution is mostly about technology and economics. The second revolution is about morality and human purposes. The biophilia revolution is about the combination of reverence for life and purely rational calculation by which we will *want* to both be efficient and live sufficiently. It is about finding our rightful place on earth and in the community of life, and it is about citizenship, duties, obligations, and celebration.

There are two formidable barriers standing in our way. The first is the problem of denial. We have not yet faced up to the magnitude of the trap we have created for ourselves. We are still thinking of the crisis as a set of problems that are, by definition, solvable with technology and money. In fact we face a series of dilemmas that can be avoided only through wisdom and a higher and more comprehensive level of rationality than we have yet shown. Better technology would certainly help; however, our crisis is not fundamentally one of technology but one of mind, will, and spirit. Denial must be met by something like a worldwide ecological "perestroika," predicated on the admission of failure: the failure of our economics, which became disconnected from life; the failure of our politics, which lost sight of the moral roots of our commonwealth; the failure of our science, which lost sight of the essential wholeness of things; and the failures of all of us as moral beings, who allowed these things to happen because we did not love deeply and intelligently enough. The biophilia revolution must come as an ecological enlightenment that sweeps out the modern superstition that we are knowledgeable enough and good enough to manage the earth and to direct evolution.

The second barrier standing in the way of the biophilia revolution is one of imagination. It is easier, perhaps, to overcome denial than it is to envision a biophilia-centered world and believe ourselves capable of creating it. We could get an immediate and overwhelming worldwide consensus today on the proposition "Is the world in serious trouble?" But we are not within a light-year of agreement on what to do about it. Confronted by the future, the mind has a tendency to wallow. For this reason we can diagnose our plight with laser precision while proposing to shape the future with a sledgehammer. Fictional utopias, almost without exception, are utterly dull and unconvincing. And the efforts to create utopias of either right or left have been monumental failures, leaving people profoundly discouraged about their ability to shape the world in accord with their highest values. And now some talk about creating a world that is sustainable, just, and peaceful! What is to be done?

Part of our difficulty in confronting the future is that we think of utopia on too grand a scale. We are not very good at comprehending things on the scale of whole societies, much less that of the planet. Nor have we been very good at solving the problems utopias are supposed to solve without imposing simplistic formulas that ride roughshod over natural and cultural diversity. Except for some anarchists, utopianism is almost synonymous with homogenization. Another part of the problem is the modern mind's desire for drama, excitement, and sexual sizzle, which explains why we do not have many bestselling novels about Amish society, arguably the closest thing to a sustainable society we know. How do we fulfill the need for meaning and variety while discarding some of our most cherished fantasies of domination? How do we cause the "change in our intellectual emphasis, loyalties, affections, and convictions," without which all else is moot? (Leopold, 1966, p. 246) When we think of revolution, our first impulse is to think of some grand political, economic, or technological change; some way to fix quickly what ails us. What ails us, however, is closer to home, and I suggest that we begin there.

The Recovery of Childhood: I began by describing biophilia as a choice. In fact it is a series of choices, the first of which has to do with the conduct of childhood and how the child's imagination is woven into a home place. Practically, the cultivation of biophilia calls for the establishment of more natural places, places of mystery and adventure where children can roam, explore, and imagine. This means more urban parks, more greenways, more farms, more river trails, and wiser land use everywhere. It means redesigning schools and campuses to replicate natural systems and functions. It means greater contact with nature during the school day but also unsupervised hours to play in places where nature has been protected or allowed to recover.

For biophilia to take root, we must take our children seriously enough to preserve their natural childhood. However, childhood is being impoverished and abbreviated, and the reasons sound like a curriculum in social pathology: too many broken homes and unloving marriages, too much domestic violence, too much alcohol, too many drugs, too many guns, too many things, too much television, too much idle time and permissiveness, too many off-duty parents, and too little contact with grandparents. Children are rushed into adulthood too soon, only to become childish adults unprepared for parenthood, and the cycle repeats itself. We will not enter this new kingdom of sustainability until we allow our children the kind of childhood in which biophilia can put down roots.

Recovering a Sense of Place: I do not know whether it is possible to love the planet or not, but I do know that it is possible to love the places we can see, touch, smell, and experience. And I believe, along with Simone Weil (1971), that rootedness in a place is "the most important and least recognized need of the human soul" (p. 43). The attempt to encourage biophilia will not amount to much if we fail to decide to reshape these kinds of places so that we might become deeply rooted. The second decision we must make, then, has to do with the will to rediscover and reinhabit our places and regions, finding in them sources of food, livelihood, energy, healing, recreation, and celebration. Whether one calls it "bioregionalism" or "becoming native to our places" it means deciding to relearn the arts that Jaquetta Hawkes (1951) once described as "a patient and increasingly skillful love-making that [persuades] the land to flourish" (p. 202). It means rebuilding family farms, rural villages, towns, communities, and urban neighborhoods. It means restoring local culture and our ties to local places, where biophilia first takes root. It means reweaving the local ecology into the fabric of the economy and life patterns while diminishing use of the automobile and our ties to the commercial culture. It means deciding to slow down, hence more bike trails, more gardens, and more solar collectors. It means rediscovering and restoring the natural history of our places. And, as Gary Snyder (1974) wrote, it means finding our place and digging in (p. 101).

Education and Biophilia: The capacity for biophilia can still be snuffed out by education that aims no higher than to enhance the potential for upward mobility, which has come to mean putting as much distance as possible between the apogee of one's career trajectory and one's roots. We should worry a good bit less about whether our progeny will be able to compete as a "world-class workforce" and a great deal more about whether they will know how to live sustainably on the earth. My third proposal, then, requires the will to reshape education in a way that fosters innate biophilia and the analytical abilities and practical skills necessary for a world that takes life seriously.

Lewis Mumford (1946) once proposed the local community and region as the "backbone of a drastically revised method of study" (pp. 150–154). The study of the region would ground education in the particularities of a specific place and would also integrate various disciplines around the "regional survey," which includes surveys of local soils, climate, vegetation, history, economy, and society. Mumford (1970b) envisioned this as an "organic approach to knowledge" that began with the "common whole—a region, its activities, its people, its configuration, its total life" (p. 385).

The aim was "to educate citizens, to give them the tools of action" and to educate a people "who will know in detail where they live and how they live . . . united by a common feeling for their landscape, their literature and language, their local ways" (Mumford, 1970b, p. 386).

Something like the regional survey is required for the biophilia revolution. Education that supports and nourishes a reverence for life would occur more often out-of-doors and in relation to the local community. It would provide a basic competence in the kinds of knowledge that Mumford described a half century ago. It would help people become not only literate but ecologically literate, understanding the biological requisites of human life on earth. It would provide basic competence in what I have called the "ecological design arts," that is, the set of perceptual and analytic abilities, ecological wisdom and practical wherewithal essential to making things that fit in a world governed by the laws of ecology and thermodynamics.

A New Covenant with Animals: The biophilia revolution would be incomplete without our creating a new relationship with animals, one, in Barry Lopez's (1989) words, that "rise(s) above prejudice to a position of respectful regard toward everything that is different from ourselves and not innately evil" (p. 383). We need animals, not locked up in zoos, but living free on their own terms. We need them for what they can tell us about ourselves and about the world. We need them for our imagination and for our sanity. We need animals for what they can teach us about courtesy and what Gary Snyder (1990) called "the etiquette of the wild" (pp. 3–24). The human capacity for biophilia as agape will remain "ego-centric and partial" until it can also embrace creatures who cannot reciprocate (Mumford 1970a, p. 286). And needing animals, we will need to restore wild landscapes that invite them again.

A new covenant with animals requires that we decide to limit the human domain in order to establish their rights in law, custom, and daily habit. The first step is to discard the idea obtained from Rene Descartes that animals are only machines, incapable of feeling pain and to be used any way we see fit. Protecting animals in the wild while permitting confinement feeding operations and most laboratory use of animals makes no moral sense and diminishes our capacity for biophilia. In this, I think Paul Shepard (1993) is right: To recognize animals and wildness is to decide to admit deeper layers of our consciousness into the sunlight of full consciousness again.

The Economics of Biophilia: The biophilia revolution will also require national and global decisions that permit life-centeredness to flourish at a local scale. Biophilia can be suffocated, for example, by the demands of an economy oriented toward accumulation, speed, sensation, and death. But economists have not written much about how an economy encourages or discourages love generally or biophilia in particular. As a result, not much thought has been given to the relationship between love and the way we earn our keep.

The transition to an economy that fosters biophilia requires a decision to limit the human enterprise relative to the biosphere. Some economists talk confidently of a five- or tenfold increase in economic activity over the next half century. But Peter Vitousek and his colleagues have shown that humans now use or coopt 40% of the net primary productivity from terrestrial ecosystems (Vitousek et al., 1986). What limits does biophilia set on the extent of the human enterprise? What margin of error does love require?

Similarly, in the emerging global economy, in which capital, technology, and information move easily around the world, how do we protect the people and the communities left behind? Now more than ever the rights of capital are protected by all the power money can buy. The rights of communities are protected less than ever. Consequently, we face complex decisions about how to protect communities and their stability on which biophilia depends.

Biophilia and Patriotism: The decisions necessary to move us toward a culture capable of biophilia are, in the end, political decisions. But our politics, no less than our economy, has other priorities. In the name of "national security" or one ephemeral national "interest" or another we lay waste to our lands and to the prospects of our children. Politics of the worst sort has corrupted our highest values, becoming instead one long evasion of duties and obligations in the search for private or sectarian advantage. "Crackpot realists" tell us that this is how it has always been and must therefore always be: a view that marries bad history to bad morals.

Patriotism, the name we give to the love of one's country, must be redefined to include those things that contribute to the real health, beauty, and ecological stability of our home places and to exclude those that do not. Patriotism as biophilia requires that we decide to rejoin the idea of love of one's country to how and how well one uses the country. To destroy forests, soils, natural beauty, and wildlife in order to swell the gross national product, or to provide short-term and often spurious jobs, is not patriotism but greed.

Real patriotism requires that we weave the competent, patient, and disciplined love of our land into our political life and our political institutions. The laws of ecology and those of thermodynamics, which mostly have to do with limits, must become the foundation for a new politics. No one has expressed this more clearly than Vaclav Havel (1989): "We must draw our standards from our natural world. . . . We must honour with the humility of the wise the bounds of that natural world and the mystery which lies beyond them, admitting that there is something in the order of being which evidently exceeds all our competence" (p. 153). Elsewhere, Havel (1992) stated the following:

> Genuine Politics . . . is simply a matter of serving those around us:
> serving the community, and serving those who will come after us.
> Its deepest roots are moral because it is a responsibility, expressed
> through action, to and for the whole, a responsibility . . . only
> because it has a metaphysical grounding: that is, it grows out of a
> conscious or subconscious certainty that our death ends nothing,

because everything is forever being recorded and evaluated somewhere else, somewhere 'above us', in what I have called 'the memory of being'. . . . (p. 6)

Conclusion

Erich Fromm (1955) once asked whether whole societies might be judged sane or insane. After the World Wars, state-sponsored genocide, gulags, McCarthyism, and the "mutual assured destruction" of the twentieth century there can be no doubt that the answer is affirmative. Nor do I doubt that our descendants will regard our obsession with perpetual economic growth and frivolous consumption as evidence of theologically induced derangement. Our modern ideas about sanity, in large measure, can be attributed to Sigmund Freud, an urban man. And from the urban male point of view, the relationship between nature and sanity may be difficult to see and even more difficult to feel. Freud's reconnaissance of the mind stopped too soon. Had he gone further, and had he been prepared to see it, he might have discovered what Theodore Roszak (1992) called "the ecological unconscious," the repression of which "is the deepest root of collusive madness in industrial society" (p. 320). He may also have stumbled upon biophilia, and had he done so, our understanding of individual and collective sanity would have been on more solid ground.

The human mind is a product of the Pleistocene Age, shaped by wildness that has all but disappeared. If we complete the destruction of nature, we will have succeeded in cutting ourselves off from the source of sanity itself. Hermetically sealed amidst our creations and bereft of those of The Creation, the world then will reflect only the demented image of the mind imprisoned within itself. Can the mind doting upon itself and its creations be sane? Thoreau never would have thought so, nor should we.

A sane civilization that loved more fully and intelligently would have more parks and fewer shopping malls; more small farms and fewer agri-businesses; more prosperous small towns and smaller cities; more solar collectors and fewer strip mines; more bicycle trails and fewer freeways; more trains and fewer cars; more celebration and less hurry; more property owners and fewer millionaires and billionaires; more readers and fewer television watchers; more shopkeepers and fewer multinational corporations; more teachers and fewer lawyers; more wilderness and fewer landfills; more wild animals and fewer pets. Utopia? No! In our present circumstances this is the only realistic course imaginable. We have tried utopia and can no longer afford it.

Sources

Barfield, O. 1957. *Saving the Appearances*. New York: Harcourt Brace Jovanovich.

Berry, W. 1981. *The Gift of Good Land*. San Francisco: North Point Press.

Bratton, S. 1992, Spring. Loving Nature: Eros or Agape? *Environmental Ethics* 14, 1.

Carson, R. 1987. *The Sense of Wonder*. New York: Harper. (Original work published 1965.)

Coles, R. 1971. A Domain of Sorts. In S. Kaplan and R. Kaplan, eds., *Humanscape*. North Scituate, Mass.: Duxbury.

Darwin, C. 1958. *The Autobiography of Charles Darwin*. New York: Dover. (Original work published 1892.)

Darwin, C. 1977. *The Descent of Man*. New York: Modern Library. (Original work published 1871.)

Diamond, J. 1992. *The Third Chimpanzee*. New York: Harper.

Drexler, E. 1987. *Engines of Creation*. New York: Anchor Books.

Fromm, E. 1955. *The Sane Society*. New York: Fawcett Books.

Fromm, E. 1973. *The Anatomy of Human Destructiveness*. New York: Holt, Rinehart & Winston.

Fromm, E. 1989. *The Art of Loving*. New York: Harper.

Gould, S. 1991, September. Enchanted Evening. *Natural History*, p. 14.

Havel, V. 1989. *Living in Truth*. London: Faber & Faber.

Havel, V. 1992. *Summer Meditations*. New York: Knopf.

Hawkes, J. 1951. *A Land*. New York: Random House.

Heschel, A. 1990. *Man is not Alone*. New York: Farrar, Straus & Giroux.

Konner, M. 1982. *The Tangled Wing*. New York: Holt, Rinehart & Winston.

Krutch, J. 1991. *The Great Chain of Life*. Boston: Houghton Mifflin.

Lax, E. 1992. *Woody Allen: A Biography*. New York: Vintage.

Leopold, A. 1966. *A Sand County Almanac*. New York: Ballantine. (Original work published 1949.)

Lopez, B. 1989. Renegotiating the Contracts. In T. Lyon, ed., *This Incomperable Lande*. Boston: Houghton Mifflin.

Maslow, A. 1966. *The Psychology of Science*. Chicago: Gateway.

Montgomery, S. 1991. *Walking with the Great Apes*. Boston: Houghton Mifflin.

Muir, J. 1988. *The Story of My Boyhood and Youth*. San Francisco: Sierra Club.

Mumford, L. 1946. *Values for Survival*. New York: Harcourt and Brace.

Mumford, L. 1970a. *The Conduct of Life*. New York: Harcourt Brace Jovanovich.

Mumford, L. 1970b. *The Culture of Cities*. New York: Harcourt Brace Jovanovich.

Nash, J. 1991. *Loving Nature*. Nashville: Abingdon.

Peters, R., and Myers, J. P. 1991–1992. Preserving Biodiversity in a Changing Climate. *Issues in Science and Technology*, *8*, 2.

Roszak, T. 1992. *The Voice of the Earth*. New York: Simon & Schuster.

Russell, B. 1959. *The Scientific Outlook*. New York: Norton.

Schweitzer, A. 1969. *Reverence for Life*. New York: Pilgrim Press.

Schweitzer, A. 1972. *Out of My Life and Thought*. New York: Holt, Rinehart & Winston.

Shepard, P. 1993. On Animal Friends. In S. Kellert and E. O. Wilson, eds., *The Biophilia Hypothesis*. Washington, DC: Island Press.

Shepard, P., and Sanders, B. 1992. *The Sacred Paw*. New York: Viking.

Snyder, G. 1974. *Turtle Island*. New York: New Directions.

Snyder, G. 1990. *The Practice of the Wild*. San Francisco: North Point Press.

Tuan, Y. 1974. *Topophilia*. New York: Columbia University Press.

Turnbull, C. 1971. *The Mountain People*. New York: Simon & Schuster.

Vitousek, P., et al. 1986, June. Human Appropriation of the Products of Photosynthesis. *Bioscience, 36,* 6.

Weil, S. *The Need for Roots*. New York: Harper.

Wilson, E. O. 1984. *Biophilia*. Cambridge: Harvard University Press.